It Didn't Just Happen

and Other Talk-About Bible Stories
By ETHEL BARRETT

Regal Books Div., G/L Publications
Glendale, Calif. U.S.A.

Published by

REGAL BOOKS DIVISION, G/L PUBLICATIONS
Glendale, California, U.S.A.

Library of Congress Catalog Card
No.: 67-30248

To Michael,
who wants to know about Jesus.

My heartfelt thanks to my editor, Frances Blankenbaker. Her splendid academic background and incisive insight are exceeded only by her impeccable tact. She would do well in the diplomatic service. But her greatest talent is for getting to the heart of a problem without interfering with a writer's style, and without spoiling the poetic rhythm that is so necessary in writing for children.

CONTENTS

When you see one of these (*)
look at the bottom of the page.

Once there was a world. And it didn't just happen. It was made according to a plan. And everything else in this book happened according to a plan too.

PART 1 STORIES OF THE BEGINNINGS

Did you ever watch your mother bake a cake? She doesn't make it just any old way, does she? She puts in just the RIGHT things at the RIGHT time. If she put paint in her mixing bowl instead of chocolate, the cake might LOOK pretty but it wouldn't be good. A cake has to be made just right. It has to be made according to a recipe. It has to be made according to a plan.

The World That Was "Just Right"

Once there was a world. And it didn't just happen. It was made. It was made according to a PLAN.

In the very beginning of the Bible it tells us that God made the world. He did! And He didn't make it just any old way either. It had to be made just right. So first He planned it. And then He made it—oh, a long LONG time ago. He put everything in its place and it was all JUST RIGHT. And this is what He did.

The first thing God did was make the light. He made it by just SAYING, "Let there be light." God tells us so in the Bible. Now of course it isn't very good for it to be light ALL the time, because nobody would get any SLEEP—so God made it light only PART of the time. He separated the light from the darkness, and He called the light "day." And He called the darkness "night." But the world wasn't finished yet. It needed more. And God DID more.

The second day He said, "Let there be a sky." And there was! He stretched it out overhead, blue and beautiful. The Bible says "He stretcheth forth the sky like a curtain." So now the world had day and night—and a sky. But it wasn't finished yet. It needed more. Do you know why? It was all water! Everywhere, all over, every BIT of it was water. Now of course THAT wasn't the way God wanted it. It needed MUCH more than that. And God DID more.

The third day God gathered the water together and separated it from the land. Oh there was a LOT of water. Enough to make great big oceans. Enough to make rivers and lakes. And enough left over to make little creeks. God put the oceans and the rivers and the lakes and the creeks right where He wanted them. And He made them stay right there in their places. He even made the mighty ocean stay in its place, just as if it were a baby. "This far you may go," He said, "and this far—but no farther." And the ocean has been obeying God ever since, which is a very good thing, when you stop to think that if the ocean just BURPS, we have a tidal wave.

Then God spoke to the seeds that He had put into the dry land, and He said, "Grow." And they did! Some grew just to make things beautiful—like the lovely flowers and trees and grass and vines. And some grew things to eat—like vegetables and fruits and nuts and berries. Of course most things grew UP—like corn and tomatoes and oranges and peas. But some things grew DOWN—like carrots and radishes. And some things grew SIDEWAYS—like vines creeping along the ground. But everything grew in SOME direction. And the earth began to look very beautiful.

On the fourth day, God hung out the sun and He hung out the moon and He hung out the stars. Oh that was a wonderful day! God tells us in the Bible that the "stars sang together for joy." God put each star in its own pathway, and He said, "Now, don't you get in the way of any other star." And the stars obeyed God, and each little star stayed in its own pathway. And God hung out the sun to shine in the daytime and the moon to shine at night. That was really a wonderful day.

At last God had finished nearly everything He wanted to make. The light and the darkness. The sky and the sun and the moon and the stars. The oceans and rivers and lakes and creeks. The dry land, the flowers and trees and vegetables and fruits.

After all these things were made, God looked at the beautiful world and He said, "It is GOOD."

That means it was JUST RIGHT.

Just the way a cake has to be made. According to a plan. Just right. That's the way God made the world.

Just right.

THINK!

How big is big? How big is bigger? Biggest? Do you know how big VAST* is?

Have you ever tried to think of the VASTNESS of the

---

* Vast is just about as big as you can imagine!

universe God created? Do you know that the sun is more than a million times bigger than the earth? And that the nearest star seen at night is four light-years, or about twenty-four TRILLION miles, away? And that there are probably 200 BILLION stars in our galaxy, or group of stars? And that there are more than ten thousand galaxies, all hurtling through space at tremendous speeds — and yet none of the stars bump into each other or get into each other's way?

How does it make you feel when you think of the greatness of our God, who created this vast universe and made everything in it just right?

A VERSE TO LEARN

In the beginning God created the heaven and the earth. (Genesis 1:1)

Another verse you might like to learn: "Ah Lord GOD! behold, thou hast made the heaven and the earth by thy great power and stretched out arm, and there is nothing too hard for thee." (Jeremiah 32:17)

LET'S PRAY

Dear God, help us to understand how VAST the universe is, and how GREAT you are. And that you do EVERYTHING just right. It's wonderful to know that you are taking care of us. Thank you! In Jesus' name. Amen.

CAN YOU FIND THIS STORY IN THE BIBLE?

(Genesis 1:1-19)

Did you ever watch while your mother stirred something she was cooking? She would taste it and then screw up her face. And then she'd say, "Hmmmmm. Mmmmmm. It's all right—except—let's see. Needs just a little SMITHER more of salt!" And she'd reach for the salt to fix it up.

The First Man

God had made a wonderful world! Everything He had made was just right. The light and the darkness. The sky and the moon and the stars. The oceans and rivers and lakes. The dry land, and the flowers and trees and vegetables and fruit. This was a wonderful world—

Except for one thing.

There were no living creatures in it!

There was all that water—and no fish to swim in it.

And all that beautiful sky—and no birds to fly in it.

And all those forests and fields and hills and valleys—and no animals to run and climb and play in them.

And this is what God did.

First He made the fishes. ALL the fishes. More fishes than you can even dream of!

Tiny goldfishes and guppies
and middle-sized fishes—
and GREAT BIG fishes—
like WHALE-SHARKS!

God said, "Let the oceans and lakes and rivers and creeks be FILLED with all kinds of fishes."

And they were!

The tiny fishes swam in the little brooks. The middle-sized fishes swam in the lakes and rivers. And EVERY kind of fish swam in the big oceans, from tiny ones to whale-sharks as long as some of our houses.

God made the fishes but that wasn't all. The next thing He made—was birds. So many birds! More birds than you can imagine!

Tiny humming-birds
and middle-sized birds—
and GREAT BIG birds—
like EAGLES and FLAMINGOS and
PEACOCKS and even OSTRICHES!

And God said, "Let the birds fly across the sky—all over the earth!"

And they did!

Some birds flew around the trees and stayed in the little hills and valleys. Some birds—like the sea gulls—flew out over the water. And some BIG birds—like the eagle—flew to the highest mountaintops!

Now God had made the fishes and the birds, but STILL that wasn't all. The NEXT thing He made—was animals. More animals than you can even think of!

Little mice and chipmunks—
and middle-sized dogs and pigs—

and GREAT BIG BEARS and LIONS and TIGERS and even ELEPHANTS!

God said, "Let there be all kinds of animals—big ones and little ones and all sizes in between. And let them roam all over the earth."

And they did!

Some animals—like the alligator—stayed near the water. Some—like the monkeys—climbed the trees. And some just liked to get way off by themselves in the deep forest.

Now this was all very wonderful. Except for one thing.

There was nobody for God to talk to. Nobody to talk back to Him. Nobody in all this world for God to love with a SPECIAL love—and enjoy forever! So the next thing God did was the most wonderful of all. He said, "Let Us create MAN in our own image."

And that's exactly what He did!

God created man, and He called this man ADAM.

God let Adam live in this wonderful world. He let Adam take care of all the beautiful things. And He even let Adam give all the animals and birds their names! The Bible says that God brought all the beasts and the birds to Adam to see what he would call them. Adam named every bird, from the tiny hummingbirds to the great big peacocks. And every animal from the tiny chipmunks to the great big elephants. He gave every living creature its name!

Yes, Adam was created to care for all that God had made. But most important of all, God had somebody He could love with a SPECIAL love. And Adam loved God.

After all these things were done, God said, "It is good."

That means everything was JUST RIGHT.

Just the way the world was made. According to a plan.

Just right. That's the way God made the things IN the world.

Just right.

THINK!

God had made a wonderful world—except for what? What did He do about it? What did He make first? What did He make second? And then what did He make? And what was STILL missing? Why did God want to make Adam? What did He let Adam do?

God loves YOU with a very special love—just as He loved Adam. And God wants you to talk to Him. How can you talk to God? What are some times you especially like to talk to God in prayer? What are some things you like to tell God?

A VERSE TO LEARN

Know ye that the LORD he is God: it is he that hath made us, and not we ourselves; we are his people, and the sheep of his pasture. (Psalm 100:3)

LET'S PRAY

Dear God, we thank you that you made Adam because you wanted someone to love you. We thank you that you love US with a very SPECIAL love. And we love you, too. In Jesus' name. Amen.

CAN YOU FIND THIS STORY IN THE BIBLE?

(Genesis 1:20-31. Genesis 2:1 to 3. Then 7, 9, 19 and 20.)

Tommy is sitting on his back steps, feeling very very STUPID. Do you know why? Well, his father told him not to climb around the new building down the street because it was dangerous. Then another boy told him it was okay to climb if you were CAREFUL. So he did and—oops, one broken leg. Now he can't play in Little League. Everything had been going very well. And then he had to go and SPOIL it all. He not only feels stupid. He feels sorry. Because he disobeyed his father.

The First Lie

God had been so good to Adam! He had made a wonderful world that was "just right." And He had given Adam a beautiful garden to live in. There were no signs that said "KEEP OFF THE GRASS" and no signs that said "DO NOT FEED THE ANIMALS." Adam could do anything he pleased—except ONE THING. He could not eat the fruit on ONE CERTAIN TREE. This tree was in the middle of the Garden. God knew it was best for Adam not to eat the fruit on this tree. He TOLD Adam. "Adam," He said, "this is the tree of the knowledge of good and evil, and if you eat that fruit, it will HURT you." Well THAT'S plain enough!

God had done MANY things for Adam, but He asked Adam to do just ONE thing for Him—to OBEY Him.

And God thought of everything to make Adam happy. He even made Adam a beautiful wife, and her name was Eve. So now Adam had the Garden, the animals and the birds—and a wife!

Adam and Eve were so happy in the Garden—it didn't seem possible that anything could go wrong.

But something did. And it happened like this:

One day, Eve was walking in the Garden, when she came to the tree right in the middle—the tree that God had said not to eat from. Eve was looking at the fruit and thinking about it, when along came—a beautiful creature. This beautiful creature was a serpent.

And the serpent said to Eve, "Has God said that you must not eat the fruit from EVERY tree in the Garden?"

"Oh NO," said Eve. "God didn't say that at all. We can eat all the OTHER fruit. It's just the fruit on this ONE TREE that we should not eat. God said it would hurt us."

And that wicked serpent told the lie that started all the trouble. "It won't REALLY hurt you," he said slyly. "It will just make you WISE. You shall be as gods, knowing good and evil."

Well!

It SOUNDED so good that Eve believed it. First she picked some fruit. Then she ATE it. Then she gave Adam some. And HE ate it, too. And so they both disobeyed God.

Well, the MINUTE they disobeyed God, they began to be afraid. When God came to visit them, and they heard His voice in the Garden, they were so afraid that they HID.

"Adam," called God, "where are you?"

And Adam called back, "Lord, I was afraid when I heard your voice, and so I hid."

Now of course Adam and Eve couldn't REALLY hide from God. God knew right where they were. And He also knew that they had done the ONE THING He had told them NOT to do.

And because they had disobeyed Him, God told Adam and Eve to leave the Garden.

God still LOVED Adam and Eve. He loved them so much that He even went with them outside the Garden, to watch over them.

But nothing could be quite the same again. God had made a beautiful garden—but Adam and Eve had disobeyed—and spoiled it all!

THINK!

God asked Adam to do just ONE thing for him—what was it? What happened to Adam and Eve after they disobeyed God? What is one way God showed he still loved them? Can you think of some ways you have disobeyed and "spoiled it all"? The Bible calls it sin, and says that sin must be punished.

But the Bible has some wonderful news for you!

First, there's something you must do. It tells us what, in Psalm 38:18. ("I will be sorry for my sin.") And now comes the wonderful news. God has already sent his Son Jesus to take your punishment! All you have to do is BELIEVE that. And then let him KNOW you believe it. Tell him you want to belong to him. For the Bible says that "God so loved the world (that means you) that he gave his son . . . that whosoever (that means you again) BELIEVES in him . . . shall have everlasting life." (John 3:16.) After you've done this, do you know who you are? Why, you're a child of God! Isn't THAT wonderful news?

A VERSE TO LEARN

But as many as received him, to them gave he power to become the sons of God, even to them that believe on his name. (John 1:12)

LET'S PRAY

Dear God, thank you for sending Jesus to be our Saviour. Show us the wrong things we do. Help us to "be sorry for our sin" and obey your commands. Thank you for loving us so much. In Jesus' name. Amen.

CAN YOU FIND THIS STORY IN THE BIBLE?

(Genesis 3:1-24)

Did you ever have all your friends go off to play some-where you weren't allowed to go? Perhaps there was deep water nearby, or railroad tracks, or SOMETHING danger-ous or wrong. And your friends ran off laughing and left you alone, and there you were, the only one on the whole street who was OBEYING. Sometimes it's lonely business, being the only one obeying. It might be LONELY. But it's RIGHT. And that's what counts with God!

The Strangest Boat in the World

There is one thing God wants, more than anything else in the world. He wants His children to love and obey Him.
He does!

Remember, Adam and Eve didn't obey God and they had to leave the beautiful Garden. But that wasn't all—

Adam and Eve had children, and their children had children, until after awhile—oh, it took a long time—but after awhile, the world was just FILLED with people who didn't obey God. NO ONE obeyed God—

Except for one man. He still talked to God, and prayed to God, and thanked God for everything. And he taught his family to know God and obey Him too! His name was Noah, and he had quite a family. He had a wife—Mrs. Noah; and three sons, and their wives—and their names were

Mr. and Mrs. Shem,

And Mr. and Mrs. Ham,

And Mr. and Mrs. Japheth.

Now one day, Noah called his family around him, and he said, "Something very important is going to happen. God has been talking to me, and He has given me some plans."

"Plans?" said Noah's family. "What plans? Are they for a house? Are they for a castle?"

"No," said Noah. "They're not for a house. And they're not for a castle. They're for a BOAT. God calls it an ARK."

"An ark?" they cried. "An ARK?" They could hardly believe their ears. "Why there isn't even any WATER around here. Why would God want you to build an ark?"

"God is very sad," said Noah. "And He's told me something that's very sad. God has told me that all the people are so wicked, that His beautiful world is spoiled. And He's going to have to destroy it. He's going to send a big flood."

A flood? A FLOOD?

Why, that was hard to believe. It was even hard to IMAGINE. Noah and his family just had to take God's word for it, and obey.

And they did.

They began to build a boat.

Now this was no ordinary job. It was a BIG job. For this was no ordinary boat. It was a BIG boat. It was bigger than that, even.

It was TREMENDOUS!

This ark had to be big enough for Noah and his whole family—and that wasn't all!

It had to be big enough to hold hundreds of animals and birds, and enough food to last for a long, long time.

Noah and his helpers got to work. They cut down big trees. They measured. They sawed—zzzz-schhhhhh-zzzz-schhhh. They fit pieces together. They hammered. They lifted and hammered some more—until they had built that great ark exactly as God had told them to.

It was three stories high.

And 'most as big as a battleship.

And it had a window, way up high, big enough so that plenty of air could get in.

Yes, building the ark was a big job, and it took a long time. But finally, the ark was done.

People came to look at it, and went on their way again. They didn't care about the old ark, and they didn't care about God. And they didn't care about Noah. If they thought about him at all, it was to laugh at him.

But Noah didn't care.

He didn't care because he was busy obeying God. He didn't care if PEOPLE laughed. He knew GOD was pleased.

Because there is one thing God wants more than anything else. He wants his children to love Him and obey Him.

And that's just what Noah and his family had done.

THINK!

What does God want more than anything else? What did he ask Noah to do? Why? Did the people care? Did GOD care? Did you ever get left alone, the only one OBEYING? How did you feel? Did you think God cared? How do you know God cares?

A VERSE TO LEARN

We ought to obey God rather than men. (Acts 5:29)

LET'S PRAY

Dear God, we know that you want us to love and obey you, and to love and obey our parents. But God, sometimes it's HARD to obey when nobody ELSE is obeying. Please help us to obey, even though we're all alone. In Jesus' name. Amen.

CAN YOU FIND THIS STORY IN THE BIBLE?
(Genesis 6:5-22)

Did you ever have to obey when it didn't make any SENSE? Suppose you were walking through the woods with your father and suddenly your father said, "Stand still! Don't move. Stand—absolutely—still." And you obeyed. But then nothing happened. And nothing happened. And nothing happened. And THEN—

Your father took a big stick—and went—slowly—over —to—the—side—of—the—path—and—WHAM! Killed a rattlesnake! THEN you'd know what it was all about. And THEN you'd be glad you had obeyed.

Sometimes we have to obey even when we don't understand and even when nothing happens!

The Strangest Boat Ride in the World

Noah obeyed God.

The ark that God had told Noah to make, was finished. And now Noah was ready to begin the NEXT step of his important job. And if building the huge ark was hard, this next step was even harder.

For God had told him to gather animals to put in the

ark. Not just any old animals. And not just a FEW animals. But a father and a mother of EVERY KIND of animal in the land. And that wasn't all.

Noah had to gather FOURTEEN of certain special animals. And that wasn't all.

He had to have food and water enough for all the animals and for his family too.

Believe me, that meant a lot of animals and a lot of food. It was a BIG job.

Well, Noah did exactly as God had told him to do. He took two mice, two dogs, two lions, two elephants—

Two hummingbirds, two robins, two peacocks. Two—

From the littlest to the biggest, there wasn't one single kind of animal or bird or insect left out.

That wasn't easy!

But at last everything was ready. And then—

God told Noah and his family—

Mrs. Noah—

Mr. and Mrs. Shem—

Mr. and Mrs. Ham—

—and Mr. and Mrs. Japheth—

—to go into the ark, and to bring with them all the animals and all the birds that they had gathered together.

Now it hadn't started to rain yet. But Noah didn't wait around to see if it would rain. He obeyed God. The Bible tells us that THE SAME DAY Noah entered the ark with his family. And all the animals! What a sight that must have been!

Two chipmunks, two pigs, two tigers, two sparrows, two eagles, two monkeys, two giraffes, two pigeons, two squirrels, two—

From the littlest to the BIGGEST, two of every kind. And fourteen of certain SPECIAL kinds. That line of animals just went on and on and on and on and ON.

It took a long time. But after a while Noah and his family and the animals were all safe in the ark. And then—

The Bible says, "God shut the door." And THEN—

Nothing happened. Absolutely nothing. Nothing happened and nothing happened and nothing happened. For seven whole days. And then—

RAIN!

Noah and his family heard the first sprinkles on the roof of the ark. Then they heard the rain coming down

> harder
>> and harder
>>> and HARDER.

The water began to slosh up along the bottom of the ark. It sloshed and sloshed and got deeper and DEEPER. And then that great big ark CREAKED—and SWAYED a bit—and then—

It—began—to—FLOAT.

It was going to be all right. Noah had followed every single direction in the plans God had given him, and the ark was watertight, and balanced right, and seaworthy.

The ark floated there in the clearing for several days. The rain came down day and night. On and on and on.

Inside the ark, Noah and his family had plenty to do. They took care of the animals and fed them, and they kept the ark clean. And every day they prayed, and thanked God for keeping them safe.

And that water got higher and HIGHER. After a while, only the treetops showed above the water. And after a long while, even the MOUNTAIN tops were covered with water, and there was nothing left but water and sky. By this time, it had rained forty days and forty nights.

And then the rain stopped.

Now Noah didn't know what was going to happen next. Neither did Mrs. Noah. Nor Mr. and Mrs. Shem. Nor Mr. and Mrs. Ham. Nor Mr. and Mrs. Japheth. No one knew. But they weren't afraid.

They weren't afraid, because they DID know one thing. They had done exactly what God had told them to do. And God would keep them safe, for they had OBEYED.

THINK!

Is it hard for you to obey when you don't understand? Do you always know what your parents MEAN when they ask you to do something? Are there some things you can't do and you don't know WHY? How does this make you feel?

A VERSE TO LEARN

What time I am afraid, I will trust in thee. (Psalm 56:3)

LET'S PRAY

Dear God, sometimes it's hard to obey when we don't understand. Help us to trust you. And help us to know that you love us and care for us. And thank you for keeping us safe. In Jesus' name. Amen.

CAN YOU FIND THIS STORY IN THE BIBLE?

(Genesis 7:1-24)

Jimmy is a chronic complainer. He is never thankful for anything. Right now he's feeling sorry for himself because he can't have a pony. But there are so many things he DOES have, that are right under his nose. Can you find them? Should he be thankful? Well he isn't. He isn't even thankful he has his head. He probably wishes he had TWO heads so he could talk with his mouth full.

Noah Says "Thank You"

Next to loving him and obeying him, one thing God wants his children to do is THANK him.

And Noah and his family had plenty to thank God for. For even though there was absolutely nothing outside but water—they were all safe and snug inside the ark.

Days went by. Weeks went by. Months went by. One hundred and fifty days. Twenty weeks. Five months! And then, finally—

Wind!

Wind. Howling outside the ark. Racing across the water. Driving the water away. Making it go down faster. God hadn't forgotten them!

Indeed he hadn't. The Bible says, "And God REMEMBERED Noah and his family and all the animals that were with him in the ark; and God made a wind to pass over the earth, and the waters began to go down."

The waters went down and down and DOWN—until, one day—the great ark creaked and s-c-r-a-p-e-d—and—settled down and—came to a stop. It had landed on a high mountaintop!

It was time to get busy at last. First Noah took a raven and let him out the window. But the raven never came back. Then Noah let a little dove out the window. The dove flew back and forth across the waters, and then came back!

A week later Noah let the little dove out the window again. She flew across the waters—and disappeared. But that evening she came back. And in her beak was a leaf from an olive tree! That meant the water had gone down below the treetops.

A week later, Noah let the little dove out the window again. This time she never came back. And they knew she had probably found a tree to build a nest in, and that most of the water had gone.

Noah and his sons got to work. They took the covering off the ark so they could look out. Most of the water HAD gone. But they still waited for God to tell them to leave the ark.

And in a few weeks, God DID tell them.

What a day THAT was!

The great ark-door opened with a C-R-E-A-K. And out came Noah and his family.

And all the animals!

The animals acted all different ways. The brave ones, like the lions, made a dash for the forest. The timid ones, like the kittens, walked around in little circles, not quite sure what to do.

But Noah knew there was one thing HE wanted to do before he did anything else. He wanted to thank God. So the first thing he did was to gather some stones and pile them up and make an altar. And there Noah and his family knelt down and worshiped God and thanked him for saving them.

And God made Noah a VERY IMPORTANT promise. God said, "I will never again destroy the earth with a flood. And just so we'll remember, I will give you a sign. Every time it rains I'll put a rainbow in the sky. And when I see that rainbow I'll remember my promise."

And it turned out just as God had said. Every time it rained, sure enough, up in the sky was the most beautiful rainbow—just like a big curved bridge—shining with all its colors!

And Noah and his family were happy because God had kept them safe.

But most of all, God was pleased because Noah had remembered to thank him.

THINK!

Do you think you should be grateful to your parents? What about things they're supposed to do for you anyhow? It's their duty to take care of you and feed you. Do you think you should be thankful for that? It's YOUR duty to do chores and run errands and obey. But do you like to get thanked for doing these things? How do you think people feel when you thank them? How do they feel when you don't thank them? Do you really think it matters to God—whether or not you thank him?

A VERSE TO LEARN

O give thanks unto the LORD, for he is good. (Psalm 107:1)

LET'S PRAY

Dear God, it's easy to be thankful for special things, like presents and trips and surprises. Help us to remember to be thankful for things we don't even notice, like air to breathe and water and our houses and things like that. And above all help us to be thankful for your loving care. In Jesus' name. Amen.

CAN YOU FIND THIS STORY IN THE BIBLE?

(Genesis 8:10-22 and 9:1-19)

Did you ever watch your mother knit mittens? They didn't look like mittens at first, did they? Just needles, clicking along, and just yarn, twisting in little loops— click-twist-loop, click-twist-LOOP. Ridiculous!

"How do you KNOW they're going to be mittens?" you ask.

"Oh I just KNOW," she says, with a very smug look. "I'm not worried. I'm following directions, a step at a time. And I know the DIRECTIONS are right." And you just have to believe her. She DOES seem to know what she's doing!

The Strange Journey

Once there was a man who followed God's directions. One step at a time. And he didn't worry either. Because he knew that God was his friend, and God's directions were RIGHT. This man's name was ABRAHAM, and he lived —oh, a long long time ago. He had a wife, and her name was Sarah. He had a family—brothers and cousins and nephews and nieces and uncles and aunts—just the biggest family you can imagine. They lived in the city of Ur.

Now the city of Ur was very beautiful and very rich, and the people had everything they wanted and it seemed like an ideal place to live. But there was one thing wrong. The people in this country did not love God. They didn't even pray to God. They prayed to images of wood and metal.

Abraham used to go out under the stars at night and talk with God. It was on one of those nights that God gave Abraham the directions.

God said, "Abraham, I want you to get out of this country and go to another land. I'll show you the way." Just like that. That was the first step. And Abraham had to BELIEVE it. And he had to get busy.

What a lot of packing there was to do! Abraham and Sarah and all their servants got to work. They packed dishes and pots and rugs and blankets and tents and all kinds of food and loaded them on camels and donkeys. Then they said good-by to all their brothers and cousins and aunts and uncles and nephews and nieces—all except ONE NEPHEW. This nephew's name was Lot, and Abraham and Sarah decided to take him along.

Off they went, across the hot sunny desert. Some of them rode on camels and some of them walked alongside, and some of them kept the cattle and sheep together. There were no maps to follow and no signposts saying "NEW COUNTRY—159 MILES," and no highway patrol to flag down and ask which way to go. But Abraham knew that God was his friend and was watching over them all.

When the sun went down at night, and the desert got cold, they stopped and built a fire and got their supper, and put up their tents and unrolled their blankets. Before they went to bed, they thanked God for watching over them. And after they were all asleep, Abraham went out under the stars again and talked with God.

Abraham wasn't worried. He knew they were going to reach the new land. He knew, because he was following God, one step at a time, and God was his friend. And Abraham knew that the directions were RIGHT.

THINK!

Is it hard for you to follow directions when you don't know what you're doing and you just have to BELIEVE somebody? Should you believe just ANYBODY? It depends on who is giving the directions, doesn't it? You have to trust the person who is giving the directions. How can you show that you trust your parents? God?

A VERSE TO LEARN

Abraham believed God, . . . and he was called the Friend of God. (James 2:23)

LET'S PRAY

Dear God, thank you for being the kind of a friend we can believe. When you give directions, we know that they are right. Thank you for giving us fathers and mothers we can trust. In Jesus' name. Amen.

CAN YOU FIND THIS STORY IN THE BIBLE?

(Genesis 12:1-20 and 13:1-4)

Mike and Tim are going to pitch their pup tents in Steve's yard. They're going to play in them all day—and sleep in them overnight! It certainly looks like fun. But there is a little problem. Some of the yard is grassy and level, and under a shade tree. Some of it is out in the sun and full of bare spots. The problem is, who chooses which spot? Do you suppose Steve will give his guests first choice? How do you suppose they'll choose?

A Selfish Choice

God was a real friend to Abraham. Just as he had promised, he watched over Abraham and the people who were with him, and showed them every step of the way to the new land. And the directions WERE right. For finally —

There it was!

Just as God had promised! And what a beautiful land it was. It was just like a picture—long, rolling hills covered with grass like a green velvet carpet, and trees and flowers. And all for Abraham and his family and Lot and his family to live in!

The first thing they all did was to pile stones up and make an altar. Then they knelt down and thanked God for keeping them safe. And then they unpacked their things and began to settle down to live.

For a while it was just one wonderful day after another. Abraham grew richer and richer and RICHER, and his herds of cattle and sheep grew bigger and bigger and BIGGER—and that was wonderful.

And Lot grew richer and richer and RICHER, and his herds of cattle and sheep grew bigger and bigger and BIG-GER—and that was wonderful too.

But there was one little problem.

When Abraham's servants took their cattle and sheep to a pasture to eat grass, LOT'S cattle were there. And when Lot's servants took their cattle to a pasture to eat grass, ABRAHAM'S cattle were there. And it wasn't long before they were all mixed up. There just wasn't enough room for everybody. And so the servants began to quarrel.

"This is OUR spot!" Lot's servants would say. "It is not—it's OUR spot!" Abraham's servants would say. And they quarreled and pushed and shouted.

Then Abraham heard about it.

He knew that all that land was really his because God had given it to him. He could have told Lot to go on back home. But he didn't.

Instead, he took Lot up on a high hill, where they could look down over all the land. And he said, "Lot, let's not quarrel. There is plenty of land for both of us. We can divide it."

Now Abraham could have given Lot a little piece or a middle-sized piece of land, anywhere he chose, and taken the rest for himself because the land belonged to him. But he didn't. Instead he said, "Lot, YOU choose the land you want and I'll take what's left over."

And Lot could have been polite and remembered that it was his uncle's land in the first place, but he didn't. Instead, he looked on one side where the grass was beautiful and there was a big river—and he looked on the OTHER side where there wasn't much grass and there was no river—and he pointed to the best side and said, "Uncle Abraham, I'll take THAT side."

And he did.

He took his family and his servants and his cattle and his sheep and moved down into the very best part of the land, and settled down to live. Abraham and Sarah and their servants, and all their cattle and sheep stayed in the hills. And Abraham built another altar and thanked God for being his friend.

Abraham wasn't worried. He knew that he didn't have the best piece of land—but he knew that he had done the right thing.

And doing the right thing was what counted—with God.

THINK!

What is the first thing Abraham did when he reached

the new land? What other ways could Abraham and Lot have settled their quarrel? Do you think Abraham did the right thing? Why? He was left with the worst piece of land; why wasn't he worried?

A VERSE TO LEARN

As ye would that men should do to you, do ye also to them likewise. (Luke 6:31)

LET'S PRAY

Dear God, it isn't very easy to choose the next best and give somebody else the best. But we know that being polite and doing the right thing is what counts with you. Help us to want to please you. In Jesus' name. Amen.

CAN YOU FIND THIS STORY IN THE BIBLE?

(Genesis 13:5-18 and 14:1-24)

This is Bill and he's pretty unhappy. A few months ago his best friend moved away. And they promised to write to each other. Bill wrote his friend, all right, but so far his friend hasn't written back. Bill is still waiting for that letter. His friend made a promise and he hasn't kept it . . . yet. Perhaps he never will. When people make us promises, we can always HOPE they'll keep them. But we never can be SURE. Sometimes they get busy. Sometimes they get sick. Sometimes they can't help it. Sometimes they just forget. One thing we can be sure of, though. When GOD makes a promise, He always keeps it.

The Visitors Who Made a Promise

Well, Abraham might have been left with the poorest piece of land, but God had not forgotten him. Abraham grew richer and richer and RICHER. His herds of sheep and cattle and camels and donkeys grew bigger and bigger and BIGGER. And as if that weren't enough, God made Abraham a very important promise. God promised Abraham he would have so many children, they would be harder to count than the grains of sand on the seashore.

Now Abraham and Sarah wanted children more than anything else in the world. And they knew God would keep His promise all right. There was only one little problem. God said SOME DAY—

But He didn't say WHEN.

Well, the years went by and Abraham and Sarah got to be middle-aged, and they still didn't have children. God even spoke to Abraham again, and told him he would have so many children, they would be harder to count than the stars in the sky. But more years went by, and Abraham and Sarah got to be OLD, and they still didn't have any children. And more years went by and MORE years went by—

And THEN!

One day, Abraham was sitting in the door of his tent, when he looked up and saw three men in the distance. They were coming right toward his tent. Abraham didn't know that they were the Lord and two angels, for they looked just like any other men.

He ran to meet them and invited them to come and rest in the shade. The men sat down to rest, and Abraham went into the tent and told Sarah they had company.

And then everybody got busy!

The servants brought the men water to wash for dinner. Sarah baked some cakes. Abraham killed a calf and the servants cooked the meat. And before you could say "ABRAHAM"—a wonderful dinner was ready! Abraham served the dinner, and then the men sat around and talked, while Sarah stayed inside the tent and listened.

And that's when the wonderful thing happened.

The Lord said to Abraham, "Before a year is up, you and Sarah are going to have a son of your own, a baby boy."

Before a year was up! Not just SOME DAY—but PRETTY SOON! They were so happy!

After the visitors left, Abraham thought, "A son of my own."

And Sarah thought, "A baby boy—all our own!"

And not just SOME DAY—but within a year!

And sure enough, it was true.

God kept his promise, and before a year was up, Abraham and Sarah had a real live "squirgling" baby boy. He was fat and dimpled and beautiful.

The very first thing they did was to thank God for him. They named him "Isaac," and that means "laughter."

At first Isaac couldn't do much of anything. And then he learned to smile, and then he learned to wiggle his toes, and then he learned how to put his foot in his mouth, and then he learned how to creep, and then he learned how to WALK.

And Abraham and Sarah kept thanking God for him. God had made a promise. And it had taken a long, long time. But he had kept it.

THINK!

Do you think every promise should be kept right away? Why not? Is it hard for you to wait for a "some day" promise? Do you think Abraham and Sarah believed God was doing right to make them wait? How do you know God will always keep His promises?

A VERSE TO LEARN

God is faithful. (I Corinthians 1:9)

LET'S PRAY

Dear God, we thank you that you ALWAYS keep your promises. Help us to be patient when we have to wait. And help us to be grateful. In Jesus' name. Amen.

CAN YOU FIND THIS STORY IN THE BIBLE?

(Genesis 13:14-18 and 15:1-18 and 18:1-16 and 21:1-8)

Grandfather has lost his glasses—(for the third time since morning!)—and he has asked Sally if she would be kind enough to find them. Well Sally is not only kind enough to find the glasses, but she has offered to be extra kind and straighten out his things too. Now this is going to take a bit of doing, for grandfather, as you can see, is in quite a mess. You have to be feeling EXTRA kind to tackle a job like this!

How a Prayer Was Answered

Isaac grew and GREW. He grew to be a little boy, and it was time for him to run and play. He grew to be a big boy, and it was time for him to watch the sheep and to hunt. And before you could say "Abraham and Sarah"—(or so it seemed)—he grew to be a man and it was time for him to be married. So Abraham told his servant

Eliezer to go back to the country where Abraham's relatives lived and find Isaac a wife.

"Don't find just ANY wife, Eliezer," said Abraham. "Find just the RIGHT wife. Ask God to give you directions. And find a wife who is kind."

So Eliezer took camels and jewels and presents and food and some servants and went to the city where Abraham's relatives lived. When they got there, they stopped by the city well to rest. And while they were resting, Eliezer began to think. It was evening, and he knew that the women and the girls would be coming to the well to get water for their families. What if one of THEM was the right girl for Isaac? And how would Eliezer know?

Right then and there, Eliezer asked God for directions. "Please, God," he said, "when the girls from the village come to the well to get water, help me choose the right girl for Isaac. I'll ask her for a drink of water, and if she is the right one, have her give me a drink and offer to give the camels a drink, too. Help me find a girl who is kind."

That was really asking directions!

Eliezer had no sooner asked that of God, than along came—the most beautiful girl! She was carrying a pitcher on her shoulder. She went to the well and put her pitcher down. Eliezer watched. There was a bucket tied to the well by a rope, and she let the rope down—
>down—
>>DOWN—
>>>until the bucket went
>>>SPLASH!—
>>>>and filled with water.
Then she pulled and p-u-l-l-e-d the bucket back up again. She poured the water into her pitcher and started on her way.

Was she the one? Now was the time to find out! Eliezer hurried up to her. "Please," he said, "let me drink a little water from your pitcher."

She gave him the pitcher—and he drank and handed the pitcher back, and—

"I'll draw water for your camels, also," she said.

Well, when you stop to think that one camel drinks about twenty gallons of water when he's thirsty, and that Eliezer had ten camels with him, and you multiply twenty by ten, you can see that this girl wasn't just kind. She was EXTRA kind. Two hundred gallons of water! She was the one!

Eliezer watched her while she drew water and more water and MORE water for the camels. And he bowed his head then and there to thank God for giving him directions, and for choosing such a kind and polite girl for Isaac's wife. Then he gave her some rings and bracelets.

"Whose daughter are you?" he said. "Is there room for us to stay in your father's house?"

She told him her name was Rebekah, and there was LOTS of room for them in her father's house.

And when Eliezer went to her father's house and told her father and mother that God had chosen Rebekah for Isaac's wife, they let her go back with him!

And that's how it happened, that when Eliezer went back to Abraham, he had a wife for Isaac. Not just ANY wife. But the RIGHT wife. She was extra kind. God had certainly given Eliezer the right directions!

THINK!

Is it a good idea to ask God for directions when you're about to do something important? How about something that doesn't seem very important? Do you suppose everything you do is important to God? Do you think Eliezer was wise to ask God for directions? Do you think Rebekah was foolish to be so extra kind? Isn't it good enough to just do what you are asked to do? Is it dumb to do anything extra? Do you suppose God wants you to? What do you think?

A VERSE TO LEARN

Even a child is known by his doings, whether his work be pure, and whether it be right. (Proverbs 20:11)

LET'S PRAY

Dear God, we thank you that you are interested in everything we do—both the BIG things and the LITTLE things. And we know that it's good to be kind. But it's better to be EXTRA kind whenever we can. In Jesus' name. Amen.

CAN YOU FIND THIS STORY IN THE BIBLE?

(Genesis 24:1-67)

Mike has gone to the old deserted house on the edge of town. All the kids said it was haunted.* Mike felt real brave, telling the boys that he wasn't afraid to go there. But now it's getting dark and he has just stepped on a loose board that went c-r-e-a-k—and he's afraid. Mike has disobeyed his parents; they told him not to go there, and of course you can see he is in a bit of a jam. Do you suppose God is still watching over him?

The Man Who Ran Away

Well, Isaac and Rebekah got married, and God was good to them. He gave them—not ONE baby—but TWO babies, born at the same time. They were TWINS and their names were Esau and Jacob.

God was good to Esau and Jacob, too. They had a good

---

* Of course, the house isn't really haunted, and there are no such things as ghosts.

father and mother. They had lots of things to do. They could play together and make bows and arrows and hunt.

But one thing was wrong.

They couldn't get along together. They quarreled and pushed and kicked.

When they grew up to be men, God was still good to them. They had everything—sheep and cattle and gold and silver. They could work together and make bows and arrows and hunt.

But the same thing was still wrong.

They couldn't get along together. They quarreled and lied and cheated.

One day, Jacob cheated his brother Esau—and Esau was SO angry that Jacob was afraid. His mother, Rebekah, was afraid, too. "You'd better go away before Esau hurts you," she told Jacob. "Go back to my country and stay with my brother Laban for awhile." And that's how it happened that Jacob ran away.

He said good-by to his mother and father. But he didn't say good-by to Esau.

He was afraid of Esau.

Jacob ran away without camels. Without servants. Without friends. He hurried through the stony paths of the hill country. He walked across the fields of the flat country. And he sneaked through the mountain passes. And wondered every minute if Esau was following!

As the sun went down, every shadow looked like Esau. And when it got dark, every noise sounded like Esau. Jacob curled up on the ground and put his head on a stone. He felt as if NOBODY cared what happened to him. "Nobody is with me," he thought. And then he fell asleep. He was sleeping soundly,

when—

suddenly—
there was a great big ladder, right before Jacob's eyes! It started at the ground and reached all the way up to the sky. And there were angels going up and coming down. And he heard the voice of God saying, "I am with you— and I will watch over you wherever you go."

It was a dream! Why, Jacob wasn't alone—GOD was with him!

Then suddenly the ladder was gone—
and the angels were gone—
and God's voice was gone—
and Jacob awoke.

But he didn't feel alone any more. And he didn't feel afraid any more. He took the stone he had used for a pillow, and set it up for an altar, and thanked God for watching over him. And he started on his way again—

Without camels. Without servants. Without friends.

But God was with him. And he knew he'd be all right. He knew he'd get to his Uncle Laban's house safely.

And he did!

THINK!

Well, Jacob had certainly disobeyed God. He quarreled and he lied and he cheated. But STILL God said, "I am with you—and I will watch over you wherever you go." Did that give Jacob an excuse for disobeying God? What do you think?

A VERSE TO LEARN

Behold, I am with thee, and will keep thee in all places. (Genesis 28:15)

LET'S PRAY

Dear God, we know that you are still with us, even when we disobey you. But we know that that is no EXCUSE for disobeying. Please help us to OBEY you. And thank you for being with us always. In Jesus' name. Amen.

CAN YOU FIND THIS STORY IN THE BIBLE?

(Genesis 27:41-46 and 28:1-22 and 29:1-13)

Eric has fought with his friend Paul. And here is the problem. Eric wants to make up. But he isn't so sure PAUL wants to make up. All the fellows have told Eric that Paul is still angry. And Paul is big and strong. It's taking all the courage Eric has just to go and MEET Paul. It's a real problem. What would you do? Do you think Paul will forgive Eric? Do you think he should?

Two Brothers in Trouble

Jacob went to live with his Uncle Laban, and got married and started a cattle business of his own. And then— his family grew and grew until he had eleven children and many servants. And his business grew until he had cattle and sheep by the thousands.

The weeks went by and the months went by, until TWENTY YEARS had gone by—and Jacob had almost everything in the world he wanted.

Except for one thing.

Jacob wanted to go back home. He thought about it and thought about it. And then—one day God told him he COULD go back to his own country again—and God said, "I will be with you."

A trip back home! Just imagine that!

Jacob and his family and servants packed their things and started out—with camels and donkeys and sheep and cattle and just about everything they could carry. What a cloud of dust they made as they traveled across the desert! Jacob thought of his mother and father and Esau—

ESAU!

Would Esau still want to kill him? Jacob became more afraid by the minute.

He sent some servants ahead with a message to his brother Esau that he was on the way. It was a very polite message, and Jacob waited anxiously for his servants to bring the answer. And when the answer came—

It wasn't polite—

It wasn't IMpolite—

It was FRIGHTENING!

It said that Esau was coming to meet Jacob—with 400 men! What did it mean? Jacob didn't know. But it was time for him to get busy.

First he divided his family and servants and cattle into two groups, so if Esau killed one group there would still be some left. Then he knelt down and asked God to help him. And then he sent servants ahead with a gift for Esau. A BIG gift. Hundreds of goats and sheep and camels and cows and donkeys.

And then both groups traveled on.

While they traveled, Jacob thought, "Esau—Esau—Esau—." And the clop-clop of the camels' feet seemed to

say, "Eee—sau, Eee—sau, Eee—sau"—until, suddenly there off in the distance—
Esau was coming!

Esau came closer and closer and CLOSER—

And Jacob could stand it no longer. He ran ahead of his servants and his cattle and his family. He ran toward Esau. Then he bowed to the ground. And he ran and he bowed and he ran and he bowed, until he had bowed seven times. And Esau ran toward Jacob—and he put his arms around Jacob's neck—and kissed him!

It was all over—the quarreling and hating and cheating. Esau forgave his brother and they made up, right then and there. And then they all went back home together.

Now Jacob could be COMPLETELY happy. He had his family—he was going home—and his brother Esau had forgiven him. That was something to thank God for.

And Jacob did!

THINK!

Jacob was afraid of Esau; does that make him a coward? Do you think it is all right to be afraid? It depends on the REASON, doesn't it? Do you think Jacob had good reason? Why do you think it took real courage for Jacob to run toward Esau? Esau had every reason to stay angry with Jacob, but he forgave him. What should you do when someone wants to make up with you? What can you do when it is hard to forgive someone?

A VERSE TO LEARN

Be ye kind one to another, tenderhearted, forgiving one another. (Ephesians 4:32)

LET'S PRAY

Dear God, help us to remember that it is not a sin to be afraid. The important thing is to do what's right whether we're afraid or not. Help us to forgive when other people want to make up. It IS a sin to stay angry. Thank you, God, for watching over us, when we're afraid, and when we are not. In Jesus' name. Amen.

CAN YOU FIND THIS STORY IN THE BIBLE?

(Genesis 31:3-5 and 32:1-32 and 33:1-20)

PART 2 STORIES OF JOSEPH

Well, you can see at a glance that Bruce isn't very happy. The reason is Carl and his brand new paddle-board. Carl is wobbly but happy. And Bruce is thinking thoughts like, "I could ride one as well as he," and "I hope he breaks his leg," and "Well, at least I hope he falls off." Well, it IS hard to rejoice when somebody else gets something you've been wanting for practically AGES.

The Gift That Caused Trouble

Now ordinarily a gift is a very jolly thing. You open it and you are jolly and you thank the one who gave it to you and he is jolly and you show it to your friends and they are jolly and there you have it; nothing but fun and happiness. Everybody knows that. But the gift in this story was NOT ordinary. This gift brought nothing but trouble—to a boy named Joseph.

Joseph lived way back in Bible times, and he was the happiest, bubbliest boy you could ever imagine. He was tall and strong, and he could leap over a wall or scramble through the bushes faster than the best of them. He had ten BIG brothers and one baby brother, and when they all sat around the breakfast table and passed the barley cakes and honey, there was always plenty of excitement.

Their father Jacob was very rich, and the sheep and goats and cattle and donkeys he owned were more than you could count. Joseph helped his father and brothers watch the sheep and cattle. He hunted, and he rode the donkeys and camels—and stopped sometimes to tickle his baby brother's feet. And everything was fine, until that gift came along.

When Jacob called Joseph to his tent to give him the gift, Joseph came running as if he had springs in his feet.

"What is it, Father?" he asked. Jacob held out the gift, took it by the top and shook out its beautiful folds—and there it was—splashed gay with many colors.

It was a COAT. The most beautiful coat Joseph had ever seen!

"Is it MINE, Father?" he cried. Jacob nodded yes. His eyes were twinkling.

"May I try it on, Father?"

"Of course, of course. It's yours to KEEP, my son," said Jacob. And he held out the coat for Joseph to slip into.

Joseph felt the soft, fine cloth slither over his shoulders. He looked down at the gay colors in amazement. The coat went clear to his ankles! And it had long sleeves! Ordinary coats were shorter and had short sleeves. Clearly, this was a most extraordinary gift!

"It's the most beautiful coat I've ever seen, Father! Why, only favorite sons wear coats like this!" And he thanked his father and scampered off to show his brothers the gift.

But his brothers didn't say it was beautiful. They scowled — hrummmmf — and they mumbled — mumbl-mumblmumbl—and scuffed the ground with their feet.

They were angry. And they were jealous. Joseph went back to the tent, the springs gone from his feet.

Yes—a gift is supposed to bring happiness. But this one brought nothing but trouble. Trouble to a boy named Joseph and to his whole family. Because Joseph's brothers were jealous.

But Joseph knew that God was watching over him and that God would take care of him. And God did.

THINK!

What makes people jealous? Do you think Joseph's brothers had good reason to be jealous? After all, they WERE older; perhaps one of them should have gotten the coat. Even if we have a REASON to be jealous—what does God want us to do?

A VERSE TO LEARN

These things I command you, that ye love one another. (John 15:17)

LET'S PRAY

Dear God, help us to be GLAD when somebody else gets a gift, even if it's something we wanted ourselves. And even if we have a good REASON to be jealous help us not to be. We thank you for all the good things you give us. In Jesus' name. Amen.

CAN YOU FIND THIS STORY IN THE BIBLE?

(Genesis 37:1-4)

Not again! Every week Ray has some new honor heaped upon him. First he got the citizenship award, then he got the highest marks in the class for all last month. And as if THAT weren't enough, now he's going to be a safety patrolman this month. Art is FURIOUS. "He's going to tell me when I can cross the street?" says Art. "Not ME he isn't!"

The Dreams That Caused Trouble

Joseph had everything that a boy could want. But there was one thing wrong. His brothers were jealous. They were jealous because their father Jacob loved Joseph the best. They were jealous because Jacob gave Joseph a beautiful coat. And, as if that weren't enough, two OTHER things happened to make them jealous! Two dreams! and Joseph dreamed them.

The first dream was a strange one. Joseph probably told

his brothers about it at breakfast.

"Know what?" said Joseph. "I had the most amazing dream last night." And he reached for the barley cakes. "In my dream, we were all tying grain up in bundles. And MY bundle stood up straight. But YOUR bundles—" He asked for the honey. His brothers watched him.

"And our bundles? What did our bundles do?" they asked. Joseph poured his honey on his barley cakes. "YOUR bundles—" he said, "bowed down to MY bundle."

Nobody said anything for a minute. Then they all began to talk at once.

"Do you think you are going to be a KING?" they asked. "Do you think you will rule over US?" Joseph shrugged his shoulders and helped himself to more honey. But the brothers were angry.

That dream was bad enough, but when the SECOND dream came along—Well!

"I had another dream," said Joseph. "This time it was stars."

They all stopped to listen.

Stars!

"Eleven of them," said Joseph. "And that's not all. The sun and the moon bowed down to me, too!"

THIS was too much! Even Jacob thought this was too much. "Come now, my son," he said. "If the eleven stars are supposed to be your brothers—are you trying to tell us that the sun and the moon were your father and mother? Do you think your father and mother are going to bow down to you, too?"

"WE'LL never bow down to you!" said his brothers. "Not if we can help it!" They were very angry.

But Jacob thought and thought about it. DID God

have something special planned for Joseph's life? What if that dream came TRUE?

Yes, Joseph had everything a boy could want. What if some day he DID become a big, important ruler? There were lots of exciting things ahead. And lots of trouble, too!

But God was still watching over Joseph.

THINK!

Do you have a sneaking suspicion that Joseph was a bit of a show-off? How else could he have acted over the dreams? This time even Joseph's FATHER was upset. Why do you think he had reason to be? What sort of plan do you think God had in store for Joseph?

A VERSE TO LEARN

Love thy neighbor as thyself. (Matthew 22:39)

LET'S PRAY

Dear God, help us not to be jealous, even when we know somebody else is going to be boss over us and we think he has no right to be. Help us to remember that YOU plan all these things, and that when we obey others, like kids who are safety patrolmen and monitors in school, we are really obeying YOU. In Jesus' name. Amen.

CAN YOU FIND THIS STORY IN THE BIBLE?

(Genesis 37:5-11)

Amy's mother told her to go to Sam's house to pick up her brother Peter and bring him home. Now Amy is in a bit of a dither, for Peter isn't there any more; he went to the playground. Should Amy go back home? Or go on to the playground and track down Peter? She certainly won't get any thanks for her trouble. Decisions, decisions!

The Errand That Ended in Trouble

Joseph's brothers hated him.

"Dreamer!" they said, whenever he walked past.

"Good-by, 'Dreamer'!" they laughed when they went off to another part of the country to find new pastures for the sheep and cattle.

After they were gone, Joseph didn't have any more dreams. And as the weeks went by, he forgot about trouble.

And then, one day, Jacob gave Joseph a very important errand to do.

"My son," said Jacob, "I want you to find your brothers and bring me back news that they are safe."

Go find his brothers! Why they were in Shechem—at least 60 miles away! It would mean walking all day and sleeping out at night—

"Yes, SIR!" said Joseph as he started to get ready. "I'll be careful, Father," he said as he put on his beautiful coat. "Don't worry about me," he said as he strapped his lunch on his back and kissed his father good-by. And he started out on the biggest job his father had ever given him to do.

It was dangerous and exciting, traveling the country alone. But when he got to Shechem and found out that his brothers had gone on to Dothan, it seemed more dangerous and less exciting. Dothan was another twenty miles away! What to do? Go on or go back? Joseph decided to go on.

The last twenty miles were hard going. Joseph was glad when he saw his brothers in the distance. "Now—at LAST," he thought, "the danger is over."

But the danger was just BEGINNING.

When his brothers saw him coming, they said, "Look! Here comes the 'dreamer.'" They saw the gay colors of the coat in the distance. They remembered the dreams. And they were angry all over again.

"Let's kill him!" they said. "Let's throw him into a pit and say he was killed by a wild beast."

But the oldest brother, Reuben, had a twinge of conscience.*

"No—let's just throw him into a pit alive and leave him there to die," he said. But he was thinking, "I'll come back and save Joseph after my other brothers have gone."

Poor Joseph didn't know any of this when he ran up to his brothers and said, "Father sent—"

And THEN—

They grabbed him. They pulled off his coat. They

---

* He knew that was wrong.

dragged him to the pit. And—hup!—pushed him in!

"Please—!" he called. But nobody answered. Had they gone off to leave him to die?

Joseph thought the end had come. And Reuben thought he would come back and save Joseph.

But they were BOTH wrong!

God had planned something ELSE—something neither of them had dreamed of!

THINK!

When Joseph got to Shechem he had a decision to make. What was it? How did he show that he was really obeying his father? Joseph obeyed his father and got into nothing but trouble. But there was a bright side; what was it?

A VERSE TO LEARN

Children, obey your parents in all things. (Colossians 3:20)

LET'S PRAY

Dear God, help us to remember that you are taking care of us even when it doesn't LOOK that way. The important thing is for us to OBEY whether we get any thanks for it or not. Thank you for watching over our lives. In Jesus' name. Amen.

CAN YOU FIND THIS STORY IN THE BIBLE?

(Genesis 37:12-24)

Frank has "borrowed" his brother's bike. But there are two problems. One problem is, Frank's brother doesn't know about it. The other problem is, Frank is returning the bike with something it didn't have before; a nice big dent! Now Frank is sneaking the bike back in the garage, hoping his brother won't notice. It was bad enough for Frank to "borrow" the bike. But now that he's done it, he ought to at least have the courage to face up to the consequences.

The Journey That Changed a Life

Joseph was in the bottom of the pit where his brothers had thrown him. His brothers didn't answer when he shouted. His hands and feet slipped on the stones and sand as he tried to climb up. There was no way out. Joseph was in terrible trouble.

Now, if Joseph thought that things were pretty bad, he was mistaken. They weren't just bad. They were worse than that. They were TERRIBLE! Because Reuben was the only brother who wanted to save Joseph. And Reuben had gone away—perhaps to another meadow to watch some cattle. Joseph was alone in the pit. And the other brothers wanted to kill him.

ANYTHING could happen! And something did. Something that changed Joseph's whole life!

It happened while the brothers were eating their lunch. At first it was a speck in the distance. Then it came closer. It was a caravan of merchants. Camels and donkeys loaded with bundles of things to sell in Egypt.

"It's merchants!" said the brothers. "They're on their way to Egypt to sell—"

SELL! Why not sell JOSEPH?

"Let's sell him to the merchants," they said. "Then we won't have to kill him. And we'll never have to see this 'dreamer' again."

So they dragged poor Joseph out of the pit and shouted for the merchants to stop.

"Want to buy a boy?" they asked. "He's big and strong and will make a good slave."

"Hmmm," said the merchants as they looked Joseph over, and "hummmmmm," as they saw how tall and strong he was. "He looks pretty good. We'll give you twenty pieces of silver for him."

And the brothers sold poor Joseph as if he were a loaf of bread. They watched him as he marched away with the caravan. He got smaller and smaller. Then he was gone.

There was nothing left of Joseph but his beautiful coat.

When Reuben came back and discovered that Joseph was gone, he was HORRIFIED. He tore his clothes and cried out to his brothers— "Joseph is GONE! How can I face father? What can I DO?"

There was only one thing the brothers could think of to do. They took Joseph's coat. And they dipped it in goat's blood. And they tore it. And they rolled it in the sand.

"We'll tell our father we found Joseph's coat," they said, "and he will think a wild animal killed Joseph."

And that's what they did.

"Well," they thought. "That's the end of Joseph!"

But it wasn't. They had forgotten one thing. They had forgotten God. God was still watching over Joseph. And there were some pretty exciting things ahead!

THINK!

There WAS something else the brothers could have done. What was it? When you've done something wrong, which is easier—to confess it or to try to "cover it up?" Which is right?

A VERSE TO LEARN

Lie not one to another. (Colossians 3:9)

LET'S PRAY

Dear God, help us to choose to do what's RIGHT when we are tempted to do wrong. But when we HAVE done something wrong, give us the courage to confess it and not go running around like sissies, trying to cover it up. In Jesus' name. Amen.

CAN YOU FIND THIS STORY IN THE BIBLE?

(Genesis 37:25-30)

Fanny's mother has taken her to the doctor. And the doctor has just told her that she will be blind for the rest of her life. But she is NOT about to go off in a corner and sulk. She intends to dig in and OBEY. Do you know something? This is a true story. It really happened. Fanny grew up OBEYING instead of sulking—and she wound up writing over six thousand hymns. And some of the songs we sing today in church are written by Fanny Crosby! God watched over her, and because she OBEYED, he gave her a very special job to do!

A Terrible Lie

"Where's Joseph?"

Joseph's wicked brothers knew that would be the first thing their father Jacob would ask.

Where WAS Joseph?

Why, even his brothers didn't know for sure. They had sold him to a caravan of merchants, and he was gone off to Egypt—gone forever. There was nothing left of him but his beautiful coat. And that wasn't beautiful any more. The brothers had torn it and dipped it in blood.

A few days later the brothers started back home to

their father Jacob. Where was Joseph? Well, it certainly looked like the end of him.

When the wicked brothers got home to their father, sure enough, the first thing he asked was, "Where's Joseph?"

"Joseph?" they said. "We don't know. We haven't seen him."

Jacob was frightened. "Why, I sent him to look for you! Where is he?"

Then the brothers took out the coat, all torn and dirty. They pretended to be worried as they handed it to Jacob.

"We found this coat," they said. "Do you know if this is Joseph's coat?"

With trembling hands, Jacob took the coat. He looked at its beautiful colors, all dirty. And he began to cry.

"It's Joseph's coat," he cried. "It's my son's beautiful coat. He has been killed by wild animals!"

"My son is dead!" he moaned. And he went weeping into his tent.

The brothers looked at each other. "The lie has worked," they thought. "That is the end of Joseph."

But it wasn't the end—it was a new beginning! For at that very moment Joseph was being taken to Egypt. Egypt—with houses and temples instead of tents! And streets and shops and crowds of people! And a slave market!

Ah yes, the slave market. That's where he was taken. And that's where he was SOLD. He was sold as a slave, to a man named Potiphar. But God was still watching over Joseph. For Potiphar was rich. And Potiphar was important. In fact, Potiphar was an officer of the King! And what happened?

Well, Joseph worked hard, and Potiphar was kind to

him, Joseph worked harder still, and Potiphar began to trust him. Joseph worked harder than EVER—and finally —Potiphar made him master over all the other slaves in his house!

Back in Joseph's own country, his father thought, "Joseph is dead." And his wicked brothers secretly thought, "We wonder where he is."

Where was Joseph? They didn't really know. But God knew. And God knew, too, that He was going to be with Joseph every minute!

THINK!

How is God showing that he is still watching over Joseph? Do you suppose Joseph believes that he is? How is Joseph showing it?

A VERSE TO LEARN

Fear thou not; for I am with thee: ... I will help thee. (Isaiah 41:10)

LET'S PRAY

Dear God, even when everything is going WRONG, help us to show that we still believe you, by OBEYING cheerfully instead of going off in a corner and SULKING. And help us to always remember that you are with us. In Jesus' name. Amen.

CAN YOU FIND THIS STORY IN THE BIBLE?

(Genesis 37:31-36)

Bill is on a hike in the canyon with Terry. At least that's the way it started out. Terry promised Bill that he could get them back out of the canyon again, but now it's getting dark and they're lost. It isn't that Terry WON'T keep his promise; it's that he CAN'T, for he's as lost as Bill is. What they don't know is, that there's a search party just on the other side of the ridge, coming in their direction. God is watching over them. But right now things look pretty grim!

The Dream That Was Almost Forgotten

The Lord was with Joseph in Potiphar's house. Potiphar was kind to Joseph and made him captain over all his slaves. And then something happened to spoil it all!

It was another lie. This time it was Potiphar's wife who told the lie. She told Potiphar that Joseph had done something very wicked. And Potiphar believed her and put Joseph in—of all places—PRISON!

This was REAL trouble. But Joseph had been in trouble before, and by this time he knew that the best thing to do in trouble was to behave himself. He worked hard, and the jailer was kind to him. He worked harder still, and the jailer began to trust him. He worked harder than EVER—and the jailer made him captain over all the other prisoners!

Joseph wondered, as the months went by, if he would ever get out of prison. He knew they wouldn't let him out for no reason at all. Something SPECIAL would have to happen. And something did. It was another dream.

This time it wasn't Joseph who had the dream. It was another prisoner. He was the butler to Pharaoh, the great king of Egypt, and he had such a strange dream that he told Joseph about it.

"I dreamed," he said, "that there was a vine in front of me. It had three branches. First the vine had buds on it, and then flowers—and then grapes! I squeezed the grape juice into a cup and gave it to Pharaoh. What does this dream mean?"

"It means," said Joseph, "that in three days you will be out of prison and back to your job as butler in the palace."

And it happened—just as Joseph said it would! Three days later, Pharaoh had a birthday party and sent for his butler to come back to the palace!

"Now," said Joseph, as the butler left, "will you do me a favor? Will you tell the king I have done no wrong, and ask him to get me out of this prison?"

The butler promised and went happily on his way.

The days went by, and Joseph waited.

The weeks went by,
and the months—
and STILL Joseph waited.

The butler had forgotten his promise! And Joseph thought the dream was forgotten, and he wouldn't get out of prison after all. But he was wrong.

The butler had forgotten him. But GOD hadn't forgotten him. And God knew the butler would some day remember that dream, even if it took a long, LONG time.

THINK!

Things look pretty grim for Joseph, don't they? He's depending on somebody's promise, to get out of prison. Whose? Do you think that might be a mistake? Why? Can people always keep their promises? Does God? Who is really watching over Joseph—God or the butler?

A VERSE TO LEARN

God will be with thee; he will not fail thee, nor forsake thee. (I Chronicles 28:20)

LET'S PRAY

Dear God, we know that some people don't keep their promises because they WON'T and some people don't keep their promises because they CAN'T. But you always keep your promises no matter what. Thank you for watching over Joseph. And thank you for watching over us. In Jesus' name. Amen.

CAN YOU FIND THIS STORY IN THE BIBLE?

(Genesis 39:1-23 and 40:1-23)

Jack is studying. And when he gets his lesson done that won't be the end of it. There'll be another lesson tomorrow. And after grade school there'll be Junior High. Then High School. Then College. Then pre-medical school. Then studying in a hospital. For Jack wants to be a doctor and, phew! There is no END to the getting ready! You can't just do an important job at the drop of a hat. You have to take a long long time to get READY.

The Dream That Set a Prisoner Free

God had not forgotten Joseph. God knew that the butler would remember the dream, even if it took a long time.

Joseph waited for weeks. He waited for months. He waited and waited—until TWO WHOLE YEARS went by!

And then a strange thing happened. It was another dream.

This time it was Pharaoh, the king of Egypt, who had the dream. It was a strange dream, and none of Pharaoh's wise men could tell what it meant. Then—at last—the butler remembered Joseph. And the dream. And his promise! Right then and there he told the Pharaoh that

Joseph could tell him what his dream meant. "Send for him," cried the Pharaoh, "at once!" And that's how it happened that one minute Joseph was in prison and the next minute he was shaving and changing his clothes—and the NEXT thing he knew, he was standing before the king!

"I dreamed," the king told Joseph, "that I saw seven fat cows come out of the river. Then seven thin cows came out of the river. And right before my eyes, the thin cows ate up the fat cows.

"Then I went back to sleep and dreamed another dream. I saw seven fat ears of corn growing on one stalk. Then seven bad ears of corn came up. And right before my eyes, the seven bad ears ate up the good ears. What does it mean?"

"It means," said Joseph, "that for seven years there will be lots to eat in the land. Then—for seven years there will be famine."

Famine! Why that meant that nothing would grow. There wouldn't be any grain. And the people wouldn't have any food!

Pharaoh was worried. "What shall we do, Joseph?" he asked.

"Well," said Joseph, "the first seven years you'll have more than you need. God wants you to save what's left over and store it in big barns. Then when the famine comes, you'll have enough food. You must find a very wise man to see that the food is saved."

Pharaoh thought a minute. Then he looked at Joseph. "You," he said. "You are JUST the man."

Pharaoh took off his ring. He put it on Joseph's finger. And he said, "I hereby make you the man in charge of all Egypt."

Just like that. In a moment, Joseph was changed from a poor prisoner to the head man in all Egypt, next to the king!

He traveled over Egypt, making the people build big barns and store food. He lived in a palace. And nobody in Egypt was more powerful than Joseph, except the king. At last things were going well with Joseph!

Yes, it took a long time. But God was certainly watching over Joseph, every step of the way.

THINK!

Well, Joseph waited a long time before he found out what God was up to, didn't he? Can you remember some of the things that happened to get Joseph to Egypt? Why do you suppose God did it in such a roundabout way? Why didn't he just let Joseph get on a camel and go be the head man in Egypt without going to all that trouble?

A VERSE TO LEARN

Have faith in God. (Mark 11:22)

LET'S PRAY

Dear God, it takes such a long time to grow up and be wise and strong. Help us to be willing to learn every little lesson along the way. Help us not to be in too much of a hurry. In Jesus' name. Amen.

CAN YOU FIND THIS STORY IN THE BIBLE?

(Genesis 41:1-57)

Bob is taking a second test after school. He didn't miss the first test. And he didn't fail the first test. As a matter of fact, he CHEATED on the first test. And now he's in trouble. The teacher is being a bit rough on him, for he must be taught a lesson. But do you know something? Underneath it all, that teacher really loves him. Really!

An Old Dream That Came True

God had thought of everything. Joseph was ruler over all Egypt, next to the king. For seven years, he made the people store food in big barns. And then the Pharaoh's dream began to come true.

Famine!

Just as Joseph had said, the grain didn't grow—and there wasn't any food anywhere—except in the big barns.

People came from all over the country to buy food. They came from other countries too, for the famine was all over the land.

And then, one day—another dream began to come true. It was Joseph's own dream—the one he'd had so many years before! And this is how it happened.

One day Joseph was selling grain from one of the big barns. The people were streaming in from everywhere. Joseph watched them as they bought their food and hurried on their way. And then—

suddenly—

his heart almost stopped beating. Out of the crowds came ten shepherds who looked as if they had traveled a long way. They looked familiar.

They came closer—and Joseph thought, "Could they be?" They knelt down before him and bowed their heads to the ground—and Joseph thought, "They ARE. They are my brothers!" And they WERE his brothers—all there except his youngest brother, Benjamin.

Joseph thought of his dream, which was coming true right before his eyes. His brothers were bowing down to him, just as the eleven bundles of grain and the eleven stars had, in his dream!

Eleven.

But there were only ten brothers there. Where was Benjamin? And where was his father? Joseph had to find out without letting his brothers know who he was.

"Who are you?" he said. "Where do you come from?"

"We are from Canaan," they said, bowing lower than ever.

"You are spies!" cried Joseph, pretending to be angry. And he asked them all sorts of questions with a scowling face but he didn't tell them who he was. And they quaked and trembled as they answered. And he found out—

Benjamin was alive.

His father was alive.

And none of them had any food.

Well, for the next few days, those poor brothers didn't know whether they were coming or GOING. First Joseph told them he would send one of them home to get their brother Benjamin while the rest of them waited in Egypt. Then he put them all in prison! THEN—at the end of three days, he told them they could ALL go home but Simeon. By this time they were thoroughly confused and very frightened.

"Leave Simeon here," he said. "The rest of you go home and take some food, but bring your youngest brother back. Then I'll know if you're telling the truth."

"This is what we deserve," said the brothers, "for selling poor Joseph to be a slave and for telling our father a lie." They spoke in their own language. They didn't think the great Egyptian ruler could understand them.

But the great Egyptian ruler DID understand them. For he was their own brother Joseph.

God had provided food, even for the wicked brothers. But before they got home, they were in for a surprise. And God was going to make the REST of Joseph's dream come true, too!

THINK!

Joseph was certainly hard on his brothers. He put them through three or four very bad days. Why do you suppose he did this? How do you suppose the brothers felt when they had to leave Simeon behind in prison? Underneath all this trouble, was God's kindness. What had God really done for the wicked brothers? Whom did He use to do this?

A VERSE TO LEARN

O give thanks unto the Lord; for he is good. (Psalm 136:1)

LET'S PRAY

Dear God, you went to a great deal of trouble to take care of Joseph, and then used Joseph to take care of his father and brothers. We thank you that you watch over us, even though we can't always understand what you are trying to do or why. In Jesus' name. Amen.

CAN YOU FIND THIS STORY IN THE BIBLE?

(Genesis 41:53-57 and 42:1-24)

This is a big day for Susan. She's the class monitor this week and she gets to choose her own helpers. Polly is back there in the corner just BEGGING to be chosen. There is one little problem. Polly has been mean to Susan. In fact, she has been HORRIBLE. But Susan decides to choose her anyway. Do you suppose that was an easy decision for Susan to make? Well, no, to be honest, it was not.

The Journey with Nine Surprises

When Joseph's brothers started back home, they didn't know they had nine surprises. Their donkeys were loaded up to their long ears with sacks of grain. As the brothers traveled along, they were half-happy and half-frightened. They were happy because they had food. And frightened because they'd had to leave Simeon behind in prison. They wondered how they were going to tell their father Jacob.

When night came and the desert pulled long shadows up over its toes to get ready for bed, the brothers stopped to rest. And that's when they found the first surprise. One of them opened a sack of grain to feed the donkeys—and stopped and stared. "My moneybag," he said. "It's full of money." He dumped it out and counted it. "I used all my money to pay for the food," he said. "But it's all here. Every bit."

Nobody knew what to say for a minute. Then they all began to talk at once. "The ruler will think you STOLE it," they cried. "What shall we do?"

There was nothing they COULD do. They went to sleep, more frightened than they'd ever been in their lives. And in the morning they went on with their journey.

When they got home, their father Jacob knew at once that something was wrong. "Where's Simeon?" he said. And they told him everything. About the ruler of Egypt. And how he thought they were wicked men. And made them leave Simeon in prison. And asked them to bring Benjamin back, so he would know they were telling the truth. And they told Jacob how they had found the money.

"Oh, Simeon!" wailed Jacob. And, "Oh, my poor Benjamin! I will not send him to Egypt. He may be killed. See the trouble you have got us in!"

The brothers didn't know what to say. They began to unpack another donkey. And that's when they found the second surprise. Another bag of money! Then they unpacked donkeys so fast their heads were spinning.

Three donkeys—
     four—
          five—
               six—
                    seven—
                         eight—
                              NINE!

And nine bags of money! Every bit of the money the brothers had taken with them!

"The ruler of Egypt will think we are thieves," they said. "We are really in trouble."

The nine surprises made them very frightened. But they didn't know the ruler of Egypt was Joseph. They didn't know he returned good for evil and gave them surprises as gifts. And they didn't know that—the biggest surprise was yet to come!

THINK!

What did Joseph do to return good for evil? How did the brothers feel when they found the nine surprises? What are some ways in our own lives that we can return good for evil? It isn't easy to do by ourselves; who can help us?

A VERSE TO LEARN

Love your enemies, do good to them which hate you. (Luke 6:27)

LET'S PRAY

Dear God, it isn't always easy to be nice to people after they've been mean to us. We need your help. We know it is one way of showing you that we love you. Please help us to remember this. In Jesus' name. Amen.

CAN YOU FIND THIS STORY IN THE BIBLE?

(Genesis 42:25-38)

Mark is protecting his small friend Terry. "Why don't you pick on somebody your own size?" he shouts as he packs a fat one. Mark has decided that it is stupid to be a bully. Besides not being any fun, it only leads to trouble, trouble, TROUBLE. How did he find that out? He used to BE one, that's how.

The Biggest Surprise of ALL

Joseph's brothers and their father Jacob had food. But they were sad. Because Simeon was in prison in Egypt. And the ruler thought they were thieves.

When it was time to go back for more food, they were sadder still. Because poor Benjamin had to go with them. "You MUST let us take Benjamin," the brothers told Jacob, "or the ruler won't even see us." And poor Jacob had to let Benjamin go.

But when they got back to Egypt, they had MORE surprises waiting for them.

They took Benjamin up to the great ruler, and stood there trembling. And then they had the first surprise. Instead of putting them in prison, the ruler told his servant to take them to his palace for dinner! "Now we ARE in trouble," they thought. "He's going to make us all his slaves."

When they got to the palace, the brothers tried to explain to the ruler's head servant. "We found the money in our sacks," they said. "We didn't steal it."

The servant smiled. "It must have been God who put the money in your sacks," he said. "I received the money for your grain." And before they could get over that surprise, he brought Simeon out to them.

It was all so topsy turvy! They all expected to be put IN prison—and instead, Simeon was OUT of prison. And here they all were, safe and sound, and about to have dinner in a palace!

When the great ruler came in, the brothers all bowed down before him.

"Is this your young brother?" the ruler asked. They told him "yes"—and they were too frightened to notice that the ruler had tears in his eyes.

The brothers were frightened all through dinner, and frightened right up until the next surprise. The ruler ordered their donkeys packed with grain and said that the brothers could go home! The poor brothers were quite dizzy with surprises by this time.

Early the next morning they started for home, feeling that they'd had the strangest adventure of their lives. But the surprises weren't over yet.

The brothers hadn't gone very far, when the ruler's

chief servant hurried after them. "The ruler's silver cup is missing," he cried. "Why have you stolen it?"

The poor brothers said they hadn't stolen anything, but they were frightened. They unloaded their donkeys—and there was the silver cup—in Benjamin's sack! With heavy hearts,* they went back to Egypt and bowed again before the great ruler.

"Please don't punish Benjamin," they begged. "Our poor father will die. Keep one of us as your slave, but let Benjamin go!" Imagine! The same men who sold their brother Joseph, were willing to do anything to save their brother Benjamin now! And Joseph knew they had learned their lesson. They weren't wicked any more. He was ready to give them the biggest surprise of all!

"Look at me," he said, "I am your brother Joseph."

Well, THAT surprise was almost too great to believe. They just stared.

"I AM," said Joseph. "Don't be afraid of me. And don't be sorry you sold me as a slave. God has made me ruler of Egypt, so that I could provide you with food." And then he hugged Benjamin, right before their eyes, and they knew he was telling the truth.

Oh, joy! It was almost too much to believe. Joseph forgave them for the wrong they had done! They all laughed and talked and cried together and thanked God for the biggest surprise of all! They were all together again!

THINK!

Joseph's brothers were actually being watched and tested, weren't they? Who was testing them? In what way did they show that they had learned their lesson? Can you

* This means they were afraid.

think of some people who watch your life to see if you are the Christian you SAY you are?

A VERSE TO LEARN

Even a child is known by his doings, whether his work be pure, and whether it be right. (Proverbs 20:11)

LET'S PRAY

Dear God, we thank you for giving us another chance to learn our lesson when we've made a mistake. Help us to remember that other people watch our lives. Help us to give them something GOOD to watch. In Jesus' name. Amen.

CAN YOU FIND THIS STORY IN THE BIBLE?

(Genesis 43:1-34 and 44:1-34 and 45:1-15)

The class play is over. Phew! And it was a great success! Mark's friends are all telling him how great he was. And Mark is a little dizzy with all this popularity. Which is all right except for one thing. Mark has completely forgotten his parents. He's forgotten to introduce them to his teacher. Or his friends. And there they stand in a corner, all alone.

The Best News of All

Joseph was together with his brothers at last. Oh, joy! That was the best surprise of all. There was only one thing missing. Joseph wanted to see his father Jacob and tell him the good news.

Joseph and his brothers shared their surprise with everybody. And the news traveled fast. When it reached Pharaoh, the king of Egypt, he sent for Joseph. "Tell your brothers to go home and get all their families. And your father. And come back here to LIVE. Give them extra donkeys and food and wagons—everything they need."

Oh, joy! Now the surprise was almost complete!

Joseph told his brothers the good news. And then they all got busy. They got together extra donkeys

and food

and gifts

and wagons—

and at last—

the brothers were ready to go.

"Don't get too excited on the way!" said Joseph, as he waved good-by.

Excited!

The brothers were BURSTING with excitement all the way! They could hardly wait to see their father and make the surprise complete.

When they finally got home, dear old Jacob just stood there staring. He couldn't believe what he saw—his sons.

ALL of them.

Benjamin.

And Simeon.

All safe and sound.

With extra donkeys.

And wagons.

Just LOADED.

What could this be? And then they told him.

"Joseph is still alive, Father. And he's ruler of all Egypt!"

Jacob just stood there, stunned.

"It's true, Father. The ruler we told you about is Joseph. OUR Joseph." And they told him everything that had happened to them—all talking at once. They unloaded the donkeys and wagons and gifts. And finally Jacob had to believe the wonderful news.

"You've said enough," he cried. "I believe you. My Joseph is still alive. And I'm going to see him before I die."

And then they all began to talk about it. They talked about it while the hillside covered itself up with shadows for the night. They talked about it while the donkeys got sleepy. They talked about it far into the night. And then they dreamed about it, while God watched over them.

For they were all going back to Egypt to make the surprise complete. And Joseph was going to see the one he loved best of all—his dear old father Jacob!

THINK!

Joseph was rich and popular and famous now, but he did not forget one important thing. What was it? What did he do to honor his father? How did that make Jacob feel?

A VERSE TO LEARN

Honor thy father and thy mother. (Exodus 20:12)

LET'S PRAY

Dear God, help us to remember what you say in the Bible—"Honor thy father and thy mother." Help us to honor them not just when we NEED them—but when we're popular and busy, too. In Jesus' name. Amen.

CAN YOU FIND THIS STORY IN THE BIBLE?

(Genesis 45:9-28)

Debbie is going to her grandmother's—in a plane—at NIGHT. Her mother and father put her on the plane at home—and her grandmother will meet her at the airport in the morning. Meanwhile she is ALONE. She hasn't had any dreams or heard any voices, but she KNOWS God is taking care of her. He has told her so in the Bible.

A Wish That Came True

Jacob could hardly wait to see his son Joseph. "Joseph, Joseph," he thought, as the families took down the tents and rolled up the rugs and loaded the donkeys and camels for the journey. "My Joseph," he thought, as they gathered the cattle and got ready to leave. "Joseph," his heart sang as he climbed into a wagon and they finally started. "Joseph—Jo-o-o-seph," the wagon wheels seemed to say as they creaked along.

Jacob counted the days. It was so hard to wait! He thought about how OLD he was, and wondered if he'd live to get there safely. He wondered—right up until he had the dream. One night when they stopped to rest, Jacob thanked God for taking care of them and went to sleep.

And that's when it happened.

"Jacob, Jacob!" It was a voice!

Jacob listened hard. "Here I am," he said.

"I am God," said the voice. "Don't be afraid to go to Egypt. I will be with you and keep you safe. And you will see your son Joseph again."

Oh joy! Oh wonder! God was good! Jacob began to count the HOURS. "Joseph, J-o-o-o-seph," creaked the wagon wheels.

When they got near Egypt, Jacob could hardly wait. He sent his son Judah ahead to tell Joseph they were coming. And then he began to count the MINUTES. Would they EVER get there? Jacob strained his eyes to see the first sign of Egypt as he joggled along in his wagon. He watched every cloud of dust, every speck.

And then one cloud of dust became a speck and got bigger and BIGGER. Someone was coming. Was it Judah coming back? Jacob looked HARD. Was it a donkey? No —it was a chariot. A big, beautiful chariot with swift horses and—who?

The chariot came nearer, and Jacob held his breath. The horses stopped by Jacob's wagon, their coats wet and shining from running hard, and sent a swirl of dust up around them.

Judah was in the chariot. And with him was a tall, handsome stranger. With beautiful clothes. And a gold chain around his neck. The ruler of Egypt.

"Joseph!" cried Jacob, hardly daring to believe his eyes. And the big important ruler sprang out of the chariot and took poor old Jacob in his arms. And they both cried together.

"Father, Father," said Joseph, "I could not wait. I had

to come to meet you."

What joy there was as they all went on to Egypt together! Joseph introduced them to Pharaoh who gave them the best part of the land to live in. All the surprises were complete at last.

And God had been watching over them all—every minute!

THINK!

How did God let poor old Jacob know that He was with him? Do you remember another dream Jacob had when he was a young man?* What was the very last surprise? Do you think God is with you when you go on trips? How do you know? Where in the Bible does it say so?

A VERSE TO LEARN

The LORD hath done great things for us; whereof we are glad. (Psalm 126:3)

LET'S PRAY

Dear God, we know you are always watching over us. Even though we don't have dreams or hear voices or see angels or things like that. You have told us so in the Bible. Help us to remember this. And thank you. In Jesus' name. Amen.

CAN YOU FIND THIS STORY IN THE BIBLE?

(Genesis 46:1-34 and 47:1-12)

---

* It's in one of the very first stories.

PART 3 STORIES OF MOSES

Becky can't play this afternoon. She's stuck with her baby brother. She has to watch him while her mother gets some important things done in the house. How do you think Becky feels about it? Well, if you want to know the truth, she doesn't feel "stuck" at all. Actually she has a sneaky feeling of joy. It's really fun to take care of a baby. And it's WONDERFUL to be trusted with one!

A Secret in a Basket

Most big brothers and sisters help take care of the baby in the house or on the porch or in the yard. Can you imagine taking care of your baby brother while he's sleeping—in the RIVER? That happened once, to a big sister named Miriam. She took care of her baby brother, and it was no easy job. Because she lived long long ago—not in ORDINARY times. She lived in time of TROUBLE.

The trouble all began with a wicked king, called Pharaoh. The people of Israel lived in his land. They were

God's people, and Pharaoh hated them. He made them all slaves, and had his soldiers beat them, to make them work hard. The harder they worked, the more they were beaten —and the more they were beaten, the stronger they grew!

"They grow stronger every day," said Pharaoh, and he ordered his soldiers to beat them harder. "They grow stronger than EVER," cried Pharaoh, and he gave an order—

"Every baby boy born to the people of Israel shall be killed!"

What terrible news! It sent the people of Israel scurrying into their houses. Of course they already knew that Pharaoh hated them—but this! This was the worst news of all. Everybody listened. Mothers and fathers listened. And brothers and sisters listened.

There was one big sister and little brother who listened HARD. Their names were Miriam and Aaron. They listened hard, and then they went scurrying into THEIR house. For they HAD a brand new baby brother!

Miriam and Aaron and their mother looked at the baby.

There he lay—all little and pink and sound asleep. Aaron was too little to understand—but Miriam and her mother both thought the same thing. "We must keep him QUIET," they thought—"so Pharaoh's soldiers won't know he's here!"

After that, taking care of their brother was no easy job. They fed him before he was even hungry—and they rocked him before he was even sleepy. They did EVERY-THING to keep him from crying. And every time the soldiers went by, they asked God to keep him from crying, so he wouldn't be found.

Of course, the baby couldn't stay little and pink and sound asleep forever. He found his fingers and put them in his mouth—and gurgled. Then he got bigger and found his FEET and put them in his mouth—and SQUEALED. Then he got bigger, and kicked his blankets off—and LAUGHED! Something had to be done!

Miriam knew her mother would think of SOMETHING. But what her mother thought of, sent little prickles of fear right down Miriam's back! For this is what her mother did. She took some reeds, and wove a little basket, just like a cradle. She filled up the cracks with tar. "So it won't leak," she said.

"Leak?" said Miriam. "Where are you going to PUT him?"

"In the river," said her mother, and the prickles of fear came back again, up and down Miriam's back.

And sure enough—that's just what they did. Early the next morning they put baby Moses in the basket—and asked God to take care of him. Then they went down to the river and the mother waded out and tucked that little basket in among the tall grasses, called bulrushes, that were growing up out of the water.

"You stay close by," whispered Miriam's mother, "and watch him from the shore." And then she was gone.

Miriam watched and waited. She waited while the prickles of fear went up and down her back. She waited until—

VOICES!

Miriam held her breath. Were they soldiers? No—they were WOMEN'S voices! "Dear God," prayed Miriam, "take care of my baby brother, no matter WHAT happens!"

Miriam didn't know what WOULD happen, because the order from the king had been, "Every baby boy shall be killed!"

But she DID know that GOD was watching over that baby and that He would keep him safe.

THINK!

Miriam didn't know what was going to happen, but she trusted someone. Whom? That was a long time ago. Do you think we can trust the same one today? What are some times you didn't know what was going to happen, but you trusted God to help you?

A VERSE TO LEARN

Casting all your care upon him; for he careth for you. (I Peter 5:7)

LET'S PRAY

Dear God, we thank you that you still take care of us today the same way you took care of your children back in Bible times. Help us to trust you no matter WHAT happens. In Jesus' name. Amen.

CAN YOU FIND THIS STORY IN THE BIBLE?

(Exodus 1:1-22 and 2:1-3)

Gary has to screw up all his courage, for this is a bad moment. He is moving to a big city in an apartment—where they don't allow pets. And he has to give his puppy away. This is the moment, at last, to say good-by. It isn't easy. But Gary knows his puppy will be safe in a new home. And that's what counts.

A Surprise for a Princess

It certainly looked as if baby Moses didn't have a chance. There he was, rocking back and forth in a basket in the river. And there was his big sister Miriam watching from the shore. SHE couldn't help him. But God could!

When Miriam heard the women's voices, she crept through the reeds to peek—and stopped in her tracks. "It's the PRINCESS!" she gasped. "She's coming to bathe in the river!"

Sure enough, it was! Her beautiful dress was purple and gold. Her rings and bracelets glittered in the sunlight. Her maidens fanned her with large fans. She was a princess all right—and her father was THE WICKED PHARAOH!

Miriam looked back at the basket. It was rocking back and forth—"oh dear," thought Miriam. "Is he awake? Is he KICKING? Oh DEAR!" And she thought, "Baby, be quiet—PLEASE be quiet!" And then—

"What is that, floating over there?" It was the princess speaking. She has seen the basket! Miriam's heart almost stopped beating. She stumbled closer, and listened while the princess asked one of her maidens to bring the basket to her. She watched while the maiden waded over and got the basket. She held her breath while the princess and her maidens looked inside. The baby kicked his little feet. He doubled up his little fists. He puckered up his little face. And he cried! Oh, he cried HARD! Miriam almost fell over her own feet, to get closer.

"It's one of the Hebrew babies—it belongs to one of the people of Israel," said the princess, as she picked him up. "He's a beautiful baby," she crooned, as she held him close.

The maidens stood around, all excited. "What are you going to DO with him?" they asked.

The princess looked at the baby. The baby stopped crying for a minute, and looked at the princess. And then—

"I—I'm going to keep him," she said. "I'm going to call him Moses." Baby Moses began to cry again, as if this wasn't good news at all. But Miriam knew it was the best news in the world!

"You'll have to find him a nurse," said the maidens. And Miriam stumbled out of the reeds before she had time to even be frightened. She bowed to the princess—and her legs got all tangled up like a pretzel, she was so excited.

"Oh, princess!" she cried. "I know where you can get him a nurse!" And the princess looked at Miriam for a moment, and said—"All right. Go get me a nurse."

Miriam ran back to her mother so fast she could hardly get her breath, to tell her mother the wonderful news. And Miriam and her mother hurried back down to the river so fast—so fast! And at last they stood trembling before the princess.

"Take care of this baby for me," said the princess. "And I will pay you well." And she put baby Moses right where he belonged—right back in his mother's arms! Moses stopped crying, just as if he knew everything was going to be all right. And everything WAS all right! Moses snuggled up in his mother's arms—safe from the wicked Pharaoh's soldiers. Miriam and her mother had their baby back again, and the soldiers couldn't kill him now. He belonged to Pharaoh's daughter—the princess!

Yes, for awhile it had certainly looked as if baby Moses was in trouble. But God was watching out for him—and there were exciting things ahead!

THINK!

Miriam and her mother had to give baby Moses away for his own good. Have you ever had to part with something when it really HURT? (No—not a tooth; don't be smart.) Miriam certainly got the job done, didn't she? In order to get a job done you have to be in the right place at the right time. Can you think of times when you got a job done because you obeyed? Or times when jobs didn't get done because you disobeyed?

A VERSE TO LEARN

Serve the LORD with all your heart. (I Samuel 12:20)

LET'S PRAY

Dear God, help us to remember that when we obey, we're in the RIGHT place at the RIGHT time. Thank you for doing everything for our own good, even if it means that sometimes we have to give up something. In Jesus' name. Amen.

CAN YOU FIND THIS STORY IN THE BIBLE?

(Exodus 2:5-10)

Karen is going off to camp. For the whole summer. And she's going to be with strangers—people she's never even SEEN before! Her head is chock-full of instructions. Mother has given her instructions. And grandmother has. And father has. And if her dog could talk, he would have, too. Her head is so loaded with instructions she feels TOP-heavy. It's going to be a long summer. Karen hopes she can remember HALF of them.

The Boy Who Became a Prince

Baby Moses belonged to the Pharaoh's daughter—a real live princess! And he had for a nurse—his own mother! And he lived—in his own house! How happy everybody was! Now Moses could kick and cry all he wanted to, and nobody cared. Miriam took him out in the sun and played with him—and nobody bothered them. It was wonderful. Oh joy!

But now they had to get busy. They had to teach him about God. They had to teach him to pray. So while he was still kicking in his basket, they crooned songs about God to him. While he was creeping around the house, they taught him to obey. And while he was learning to walk, they told him stories about God. And before you could say "Moses-in-the-bulrushes"—he had grown to be a little boy. And it was time for him to go to the palace and live with the princess.

How Moses' family hated to see him go! How hard it was to say good-by! As his mother left him with the princess, she remembered that God had spared his life— and she asked God to keep right on watching over him.

Moses looked at his new mother, with her beautiful gown and jewels. He looked at the shiny palace floors, and the huge rooms and the lovely gardens. And he took a deep, DEEP breath—and started his new life.

The fun was different. Instead of going for hikes, he went for rides in big chariots drawn by beautiful horses. Instead of playing in the streets with Miriam watching over him, he played in the palace gardens, with wonderful toys—and GUARDS watching over him.

The eating was different. Instead of helping to set the table, and going out to carry water—he had servants to bring him his dinner and his snacks on gold plates.

And the learning was different. Instead of listening to his mother, he had special teachers to come and help him learn to read and sing and do numbers and draw pictures. And there in the big palace, with all the soldiers and teachers and big marble statues and shiny floors—Moses learned to be a prince. And the princess and the teachers just PACKED his head full of learning.

But along with all the other things he was learning,

Moses never forgot the things his real mother had taught him. He never forgot the songs. Or the stories about God. Or how to pray. And every night, before he went to bed, he prayed to God.

The princess and the teachers were watching over his head. But GOD was watching over his HEART!

The princess and the teachers were teaching him to be a good prince. But GOD was teaching him to be a good LEADER. And in our next story—he IS!

THINK!

Did you ever try to pour water in a barrel that had a hole in the bottom? Well you don't have to—you KNOW what will happen. Sometimes instructions are like that— they go right out of your head as if you had a hole in it. God is trying to make something special out of Moses. What? How can Moses help? Are you supposed to pay attention to God's instructions just at home and in Sunday school? Where else should you pay attention to God's instructions?

A VERSE TO LEARN

Remember now thy Creator (that means God—and that means God's instructions) *in the DAYS OF THY YOUTH.* (Ecclesiastes 12:1)

LET'S PRAY

Dear God, sometimes it's awfully hard to go away from those we love. Especially when our heads are chock-full of "do's and don't's" from everybody. We thank you that we can trust you to help us no matter WHERE we are or how strange it is. That's a good thing to know, God. We are very grateful. In Jesus' name. Amen.

CAN YOU FIND THIS STORY IN THE BIBLE?
(Exodus 2:8-10 and Acts 7:21, 22)

Art has stopped to think something over, and no wonder! Mr. Willis, better known as "Old Crankyshanks" lives here. Old Crankysha—eh—Mr. Willis—has chased the boys off his property with loud shouts and threats that were a long way from being polite. And now Art has been elected to go ask the old gentleman (gentleman?)—to give some money toward the Little League baseball outfits! Phew!

The Burning Bush that Didn't Burn

Now anybody knows that if you run away from something very frightening, the last thing in the world you'd want to do, would be to go back to it. It would be like running away from a roaring lion—and having somebody ask you to go back and feed him your popcorn! And yet—that's what happened to Moses.

When Moses got to be a man, even though he was the son of the princess, he still loved the Hebrews, for they were his own people. And day after day, he saw them beaten and worked to death by the cruel Pharaoh's soldiers.

One day Moses tried to help one of these poor Hebrew men who was being beaten. Imagine the son of the PRINCESS helping a Hebrew SLAVE! It made the cruel Pharaoh so angry, that he was WORSE than a roaring lion—and Moses knew he would have to run away, or the Pharaoh would have him killed.

He started off into the desert—all by himself—and traveled for miles and miles and MILES until he was far enough away from the cruel Pharaoh to feel safe. And there, way off in the desert, he met a shepherd family and settled down to live with them. And there, he began a brand new life.

How different it was! Instead of wearing beautiful princely clothes, he wore shepherd's clothes. Instead of wandering through palace gardens, he wandered along the grassy parts of the desert, watching sheep.

The days went by.

The months went by.

The YEARS went by.

And Moses felt less and less like a prince—and more and more like a shepherd. As he watched his sheep under the desert sun, he thought about his own people and his old home. As he sat under the stars at night, he thought about his real mother, and remembered the stories she had told him about God.

And then it happened. The most wonderful—and the most FRIGHTENING thing!

Moses was wandering along the desert with his sheep,

when he saw it. It was a bush on fire. Now there was nothing so unusual about that—except that THIS bush was all on fire, but the leaves didn't curl up and fall off—and the branches didn't turn to ashes and drop. Right in the middle of all the fire, the leaves and branches stayed green and pretty and didn't seem to mind the fire a bit!

Moses just stood and stared. And then he heard a voice.

"Moses, Moses!" It was coming from the bush!

"Here I am," said Moses, and he stared some more.

"Take off your sandals," said the voice. "For this is a holy place." And then Moses knew. He took off his sandals. It was God!

"I know how cruel Pharaoh is to the Hebrew people," said God's voice. "I want you to go back and ask Pharaoh to let them go. I want you to be their leader, and lead them out of Egypt."

Why, that was worse than facing a lion! "I—I CAN'T," said Moses. "I can't do this great thing alone!"

And the voice said, "You won't HAVE to do it alone. Certainly I will be with you!"

And then the fire was gone. The bush was still there, but the fire was gone. And Moses was alone. He was afraid and excited, all at the same time. He knew he had a great and FRIGHTENING job to do. But he knew that God would be with him!

Once you've run away from something, the hardest thing in the world to do—is to go back. But there isn't ANYTHING you can't do—if God is with you.

THINK!

Can you think of times when you've run away from something very unpleasant, and then had to go back and face it? Can you think of times when someone has asked you to do something you thought you weren't able to do? What did you do about it? Did you remember that God was with you?

A VERSE TO LEARN

Certainly, I will be with thee. (Exodus 3:12)

LET'S PRAY

Dear God, help us to remember that you are ALWAYS with us—in the good safe places and in the scary places. And when we're not able to do something by ourselves, we can always count on you. Help us always to be ready to do what you tell us to do. In Jesus' name. Amen.

CAN YOU FIND THIS STORY IN THE BIBLE?

(Exodus 2:11-25 and 3:1-22 and 4:1-18)

Peter is helping his dad read a road map. (Peter is really getting pretty good at it!) They're lost—but only for a few minutes. Because there are signs by the road to tell them where they are, and the road map to tell them where to go. With all that help, they can't miss! But can you imagine trying to go somewhere with only a CLOUD to direct you? That's exactly what happened in today's story.

The Journey That Began at Midnight

Moses had a wonderful and FRIGHTENING job to do. But he knew he could do anything, because God was with him. And so he started back to Egypt to ask Pharaoh to let the Hebrew people go.

When Moses marched up to Pharaoh and said, "God says you must let the Hebrew people go!"—Pharaoh was FURIOUS.

"Who is God," he said, "that he should tell me what to do?"

But God punished Pharaoh, and Pharaoh changed his mind. And when Pharaoh cried, "All right! Let them go!" —it looked as if the job was DONE right then and there. But it wasn't.

The minute Pharaoh forgot his punishment, he changed his mind. "No," he cried, "they cannot go!"

So the job got harder.

God punished Pharaoh again, until he cried, "All right. Let them go!"

But as soon as they were ready to go—he changed his mind again!

He changed his mind again
    and again
        and AGAIN.

And the job got harder
    and harder
        and HARDER
            until it looked IMPOSSIBLE.

"Pharaoh will never let us go," said the Hebrew people. "Today or tomorrow or next week. We will NEVER GO." And they gave up hope—everyone but Moses. And THEN—

God said to Moses, "Tonight you shall lead my people out of Egypt. Now is the time."

Tonight!

Moses told the people what they should do. And they did it. They gathered all their things. They prepared a special supper. They stayed in their houses—quietly—and waited. It got late. They ate their special supper, standing up, ready to go. Waiting for the signal. Quietly. It got later and later and later, until it was midnight. And then—

The signal!

"Now!" said Moses. And all the families cried, "Now!" And they tumbled out of their houses. Fathers and mothers and children and grandfathers and grandmothers. With goats and sheep and wagons and carts and bundles. They were like a mighty army, following Moses. Dozens of them. Hundreds of them. Thousands and THOUSANDS of them, following Moses out of Egypt. Following Moses into the desert—

The desert!

Where were they going? How would they know?

Did Moses know? The people wondered as they marched along. They wondered when they stopped to rest. They marched on and ON—and wondered. And then —they stopped in their tracks. There ahead of them was a great big cloud. Not like any other cloud they had ever seen. "It's God," they cried. "It's God, showing us which way to go!"

And it was!

The people followed the cloud all day. And at night when they couldn't see it—but they COULD see it. Because it changed into a pillar of fire!

And they marched on, free at last. They knew God was with them day and night. For they had a pillar of cloud by day and a pillar of fire by night to prove it to them!

THINK!

Of course God doesn't lead us with clouds and pillars of fire today—but He DOES lead us. Can you think of any time when you felt that God was really showing you what to do? Or perhaps it happened to your dad or mother, or the whole family. Can you think of Bible verses in which God tells you what He wants you to do?

A VERSE TO LEARN

Teach me thy way, O LORD. (Psalm 27:11)

LET'S PRAY

Dear God, thank you for caring about us and what we do. Thank you for the Bible that tells us what you want us to do. Thank you for parents who teach us about you. Help us turn to you when things look too hard or we don't know what to do. We're glad you love us! In Jesus' name. Amen.

CAN YOU FIND THIS STORY IN THE BIBLE?

(Exodus 12:29-51)

These mice are in a laboratory,* being put through a test. The doctors want to find out if the mice are smart enough to choose the right tunnels, so they can find the way through the door into the other cage. As you can see, some of them are in a bit of a dither. In fact the whole situation looks hopeless!

The People Who Couldn't Go Backwards

Moses and the Hebrew people were free at last. They followed the cloud by day. And they followed the pillar of fire by night. When the cloud stopped—they stopped.

---

* A place where doctors make tests on animals so they can find out what makes them tick.

And they weren't afraid. They knew that God was with them. They followed that cloud across the desert. They followed it right to the edge of the Red Sea. And then they stopped. In front of them was the Red Sea. On both sides of them were big mountains. There was no place to go but BACKWARDS. But still they weren't afraid. They weren't afraid until—

At first it was just a rumble, like distant thunder. And then it got louder. And then—"It isn't thunder," shouted their guards.

"It's the rumble of chariot wheels!" And the people scrambled out of their tents to listen. The rumble grew louder. "It's the Egyptians!" they cried. "The wicked Pharaoh has changed his mind again!" And they climbed up on rocks at the foot of the mountains to see better. "It IS Pharaoh!" they shouted. "And all his soldiers! They're coming after us!" And the people gathered around Moses. "What shall we DO?" they asked him. "There is no place to RUN!"

"Don't be afraid," said Moses, and he looked toward the rumbling and saw the soldiers coming, like specks in the distance. "God will take care of us," he said, and he looked at the mountains on both sides. "He will show us what to do," he said, and he looked at the Red Sea. And then he asked God what to do.

"Lift up your rod," God told Moses, "and stretch it out toward the Red Sea." The people watched, while Moses did it. And as they watched, they saw that the big pillar of cloud was—MOVING. They watched it as it moved around, around, around—BEHIND them. They waited. It didn't move again. There it stayed—between them and the Egyptians. "The Egyptians can't get through to us," they said, "but there still isn't any place to RUN."

"Don't be afraid," said Moses. And he did what God had told him to do. He stretched his rod over the sea, and—

Wishhhhhhhh—the wind began to blow. It blew and BLEW and the waters began to pile up and UP until they divided into two great WALLS of water with a path right through the middle of the sea!

There WAS a place to run, after all! And run they did. They scrambled and scurried and drove their sheep and cattle ahead and pulled their carts and wagons—right through the middle of the sea, until they were safe on the other side.

And then they looked back.

The cloud had lifted, and the Egyptians were coming—down to the edge of the water, and through the path, and through the sea—right after them!

Moses acted quickly. As soon as all the Hebrew people were safely across, he stretched out his rod again—And with a mighty ROAR the waters came tumbling, swirling, foaming, back again to cover the path—and the Egyptians disappeared into the sea!

It was all over. The Hebrew people were safe again. Safe from the Egyptians. And the wicked Pharaoh. They gathered there on the shore and thanked God.

Even with the sea in front and the mountains on both sides and the Egyptians in back—God had watched over them every minute.

THINK!

Can you think of any time in your life when things looked absolutely HOPELESS and then, the VERY LAST MINUTE, something happened to make it turn out all right? Do you suppose God had anything to do with it? Did you remember to thank God?

A VERSE TO LEARN

With God all things are possible. (Matthew 19:26)

LET'S PRAY

Dear God, we know that all things are possible with you, that there is nothing you cannot do, and that we should trust you whenever we feel afraid. Thank you for watching over us. In Jesus' name. Amen.

CAN YOU FIND THIS STORY IN THE BIBLE?

(Exodus 14: 1-31 and 15: 1-21)

Nancy is pretty discouraged with her garden. Where are those beans, anyhow? And why don't the carrots get going? And why don't the radishes hop to it? Such a slow business! She planted those seeds a whole week ago! Now of course, God is going to give Nancy her beans and carrots and radishes anyhow, even though she is grumbling. But she's taking half the joy out of the whole business by being so impatient.

The Grumble-Mumble People

Moses and the Hebrew people were safe on the other side of the Red Sea. God had promised to lead them to a wonderful land. But first they had to go through a wilderness. No trees. No gardens. No roads. No houses. No stores. No water. Just wilderness.

They followed the pillar of cloud on—and on—and ON. And after awhile they began to get thirsty. And they began to grumble. "Water!" they cried. Grumble-mumble-grumble. "We should have stayed in Egypt." Grumble-mumble. And then—

"Water!" someone shouted, up ahead. And they all rushed up ahead, to see. Sure enough, there was water—beautiful, wet water, shining in the sun! They shouted for joy— they ran toward it—they cupped their hands and drank some—and—aughhhhhhhhhh! It was BITTER! It was so bitter they couldn't possibly drink it.

And then they did a shameful thing. They forgot how good God had been to them and they began to grumble.

"Are you trying to kill us?" they cried as they screwed up their faces. "We should have stayed in Egypt," they wailed as they puckered up their lips.

But Moses didn't grumble. He knew that GOD could help them. So instead of grumbling, he asked God what to do. And God told him. And this is what Moses did.

He went to look for a tree. Not just ANY old tree. It was a SPECIAL tree God had told him about. And he —hup—got that tree and brought it back to the water. And the people watched. And he—hup! threw it into the water. And the people watched. And they waited. And then Moses said, "Drink!"

They went—up—to—the—water—and—tasted it, just a LITTLE. Slp. Then they tasted it again. More, this time. GULP.

It was sweet. It was pure. It was DELICIOUS!

They drank and DRANK. And for awhile, they were happy again. They followed the cloud on and ON. And after awhile, their food was all used up. They began to be hungry. And again they began to grumble. "Food!" they cried. Grumble-mumble-grumble. "Do you want to kill us? We should have stayed in Egypt!"

But Moses didn't grumble. Again he asked God what to do. And when God had told him, he called all the people together.

"Why do you grumble?" cried Moses. "God is still taking care of you. At night you shall have meat to eat—and in the morning, God will rain down bread from heaven for you!"

Meat! Bread from heaven! They stopped grumbling, and waited. And when evening came—

Suddenly, thousands and thousands of birds, called quail, came flying across the sky. So many of them that they looked like a huge black cloud. And flying so low that the people could reach right up with their hands and catch them! They ate and ATE.

And next morning when they got up—there all over the ground—were little white round things that looked like seeds. "Manna?"* they wanted to know.

"It's the bread from heaven that God promised you," said Moses.

"Manna?" they said, as they tasted it. It was sweet, like little cakes made with honey. "Manna!" they cried, as they gathered it. It was GOOD.

"You must gather only as much as you need each day," said Moses. "And you must gather it early in the morning."

But some of the people disobeyed. "There might not BE any here tomorrow morning," they said. Grumble-mumble. And they gathered a lot extra. But the next day, all that they had left over—was SPOILED.

And some of the people were lazy. "Early in the morning is too EARLY," they said. Mumble-grumble. And they waited till later in the day. But the sun came out and melted the manna—and later in the day—it was GONE.

On the day before the Sabbath, Moses told them they must gather TWICE as much, and God wouldn't let it

*Which means "What is it?"

spoil. For on the Sabbath, God wanted them to rest. Sure enough—it didn't spoil—and sure enough—on the Sabbath, there wasn't any manna on the ground.

And so—even though they were the grumbliest-mumbliest people you could imagine—God took care of them and fed them every day. But they had to follow his instructions and obey him—or they didn't have any food to thank him FOR!

THINK!

Can you think of times when you've grumbled and God has given you something anyhow? Did it make you feel a little sheepish? Can you think of times when there might be a wee little excuse for grumbling? Does the Bible have anything to say about this? (Philippians 2:14)

A VERSE TO LEARN

In every thing give thanks. (I Thess. 5:18)

LET'S PRAY

Dear God, we know that everybody grumbles once in awhile, but there's really no excuse for it. Help us to remember that you love us anyhow, whether we grumble or not, but that's STILL no excuse. Help us to be thankful instead. In Jesus' name. Amen.

CAN YOU FIND THIS STORY IN THE BIBLE?

(Exodus 15:22-27 and 16:1-35)

*Little Hattie Wiatt lived way back—around 1885. And she went to Sunday school. Only the most amazing thing happened. The Sunday school she went to was so crowded that Hattie actually had to be sent home!

Now any ordinary person would have just been disappointed and let it go at that. But Hattie was no ordinary person. She began to save her pennies to build a new church! She saved and she saved until it got up to 57 cents. And then the most REMARKABLE thing happened. The pastor took the 57 cents and showed it to the people, and the people got so excited that THEY began to give and they actually DID build a new church! Those people were WILLING givers!

Too Many Gifts

A journey through the wilderness!
And the most wonderful part of that journey was the

* This is really a true story.

pillar of cloud. No matter what happened to Moses and the Hebrew people, it was always there. When it moved, they followed it. And when it stopped—they stopped and put up their tents. It was low enough for them to see. But not low enough for them to reach. They couldn't touch it, or get up inside it to see what it was like. It was a great mystery. It looked as if nobody was EVER going to really get close to that cloud. But one day—somebody did! And that somebody was Moses!

It happened this way.

One day, they saw a great mountain in the distance. The pillar of cloud went toward the mountain. Closer, closer. And the people followed. And then the cloud got right on TOP of the mountain—and stopped. The people all stopped too, and put up their tents, and camped all around the foot of the mountain. It was Mount Sinai.

One day, after they were all settled, Moses told the people he was going up into the mountain—alone. He said good-by, and they watched him go—

    climbing up, up, UP

      and getting smaller

        and smaller and SMALLER—

until he was just a speck. And then he was gone—swallowed up in the cloud!

Moses was gone for one day—two days—ten days— TWENTY days. What could God be saying to him in all that time? Twenty-five days—thirty days. It must be important. Thirty-five days—FORTY days. And then they saw him coming back.

It WAS important! God wanted them to build a church!

"A tent-church," said Moses. "It's to be called a Tabernacle. And God wants you to bring your gifts to build it.

He told me all the things we would need. Are you willing?"

"Yes!" they shouted.

"All right," said Moses. "But God wants gifts only from people who are willing."

"We are willing!" they said, as they remembered the Red Sea and the manna and the cloud and all the things God had done for them. And they hurried to their tents to bring out their gifts.

As the days went by the workmen got to work measuring and cutting boards. And the gifts poured into the center of camp. Gold and silver and rings and bracelets and earrings and pins. And rams' skins and badgers' skins and goats' skins and goats' hair cloth and red cloth and blue cloth and purple cloth—

"Stop!"

Moses held up his hands to the people. "Stop," he said. "My workmen tell me you are bringing in so many gifts, they cannot use them all! Stop! Don't bring any more!"

And it was true. The gifts were piled so high, there were more than they needed to build their tent-church. And God knew the people loved him. Because every gift was brought by a WILLING giver!

THINK!

What would you do if you'd saved up enough money for a new kite or a new doll and then you found out that your church needed money to build some new rooms? Do you think God would expect you to give all of it? Some of it? How much? What if you gave it all because your mother asked you to, but you weren't really WILLING? What do you really think God expects?

A VERSE TO LEARN

God loveth a cheerful giver. (II Corinthians 9:7)

LET'S PRAY

Dear God, help us to remember that the nicest part about giving is to give CHEERFULLY. And dear God, we thank you for giving US so much! In Jesus' name. Amen.

CAN YOU FIND THIS STORY IN THE BIBLE?

(Exodus 24:15-18 and 25:1-9 and 35:1-35 and 36:1-7)

The Sunday School contest is nearly over. And it looks as if this department is going to WIN. They're WAY ahead of all the others. But how they've worked! They've rung door bells and passed out invitations and phoned their school friends and have even gone to special classes to learn just how to do it. Now they're so excited they've decided to fix up their department. They're going to bring plants and fish bowls (with fish in them of course) and banners and some of their mothers are even making curtains! It isn't easy. But it's FUN.

The Wonderful Church in the Wilderness

God had done so much for Moses and the Hebrew people. And now at last God had asked them to do something for him. He had asked them to build a church. He had told Moses how he wanted it built—every single detail. And he had asked the people to bring their gifts willingly to build it. And they HAD brought their gifts WILLINGLY, and had piled them up in the center of camp. Now they were ready to get to work.

Of course it had to be a tent-church so the people could pack it up and carry it with them when they moved on. And of course Moses had to tell them just how to build it. "It's going to be a big job," said Moses. "Are you willing?"

"We are willing," they said. And then the excitement began!

The men got busy. They cut boards from acacia trees. They melted the jewelry down to big pots of gold and silver and brass. Some of them covered the boards with gold. Some of them made hooks of silver and bowls of brass. And some of them made a beautiful golden candlestick, and a table and an altar which were covered with gold.

The women got busy. They spun threads of purple and blue and red. They dyed rams' skins red.

The men got busy. They made ENORMOUS curtains —and used the threads of purple and blue and red to make beautiful designs in them.

The children got busy. Some of them carried things to the workmen. Some of them held the cloth for their mothers to sew. And some of them minded their baby brothers and sisters, so they wouldn't get in the way.

EVERYBODY was busy. And everybody was thinking, "Will God be pleased with his new Tabernacle?" They thought about it while they fastened the golden boards together. They thought about it while they hung the beautiful red and purple and blue curtains over the top. And while they put the goats' hair curtains over these to protect them. And the rams' skins over the goats' hair curtains. And the badgers' skins over all, so the rain wouldn't get in.

After the tent-church was all put together, they put the things inside—just the way God told Moses to put them.

First, in went the most special treasure of all. It was a golden box. They called it an Ark. And on the top of the Ark were two golden angels.

Then up went a very special curtain, right in front of the Ark.

And then in went the golden table and the golden altar and the golden candlestick.

And then up went the rest of the curtains. Everything was beautiful!

The whole TABERNACLE was beautiful. They stood back and looked at it. And waited. And wondered. Would God be pleased with it? And then—

The pillar of cloud that was up on top of the mountain began to move. It came down over the camp. Down, down, over the center of the camp, until—

It rested right over the top of the Tabernacle! God was pleased! God was THERE—right in his new tent-church!

And all the people knew that the Tabernacle was the most important part of the camp. It MUST be. GOD was there!

THINK!

What if you had planned to play with your friends all your spare time and then you were asked to do something for your Sunday school class or your after-school Bible class or for the closing night of your Vacation Bible school, and it all came crowding in and interfering with your play. Would it be a hard decision for you to make? Do you suppose it might work out if you tried to do a little bit of each? How do you suppose you would figure it out?

A VERSE TO LEARN

I was glad when they said unto me, Let us go into the house of the LORD. (Psalm 122:1)

LET'S PRAY

Dear God, don't ever let us take our church and Sunday school for granted. These people in the wilderness wanted a place to worship so MUCH that they just about wore themselves out building it. And they did it CHEER-FULLY. We are glad we have a church where we can meet together to worship you. We want to do all we can to keep it beautiful. In Jesus' name. Amen.

CAN YOU FIND THIS STORY IN THE BIBLE?

(Exodus, chapters 25-27 and chapter 30:36-38)

Well, in the first place, Johnny told his mother he would be back in the house by noon, but he's still staring at his fish-line, his mind a thousand miles away. He didn't hear the special whistle his mother always used, to call him, either. And he doesn't see her wave. All of which is a pity, for Johnny's Uncle Bill has phoned with unexpected tickets for a big-league ball game and wants Johnny to go along. It's all hurry, hurry, so it looks as if Johnny is not going to get to go. Alas, it jolly well serves him right.

Stop, Look and Listen

After the beautiful new tent-church was built, the pillar of cloud came down, down, down, and rested right over the top of it—and STOPPED. And stayed there. And the people knew that meant they were going to stay awhile, too. And they did.

They stayed and stayed and STAYED. Days went by.

Weeks went by. MONTHS went by. And if any of the boys or girls said, "When are we going to move on to the land God promised us?" their fathers would say, "Not until the pillar of cloud moves. God says we have to STOP." And so they kept watching the cloud.

It was easy enough to see. Every single person in every part of the camp could see it. And that camp was big. It was bigger than that. It was HUGE. It was as big as a city! But everyone could see the cloud. If the people wanted to obey God, all they had to do was LOOK.

But sometimes Moses wanted to tell them something special. And they couldn't tell that he wanted them, by just looking. They had to have a signal. And God GAVE Moses a signal. God told Moses to make two l-o-n-g silver horns. They were called trumpets and when they were blown, they could be heard all over the camp.

"When you hear these trumpets," said Moses, "you'll know it's important. When they blow like this"—and they blew a certain way—"you'll know there is danger. And when they blow like this"—and they blew another way—"it means you are to come to the Tabernacle. But when the cloud moves again, and you get all packed up to go—and they blow like THIS"—and they blew a very special way—"It means forward—MARCH!"

So even though the camp was HUGE, everybody could hear the trumpets. If the people wanted to obey God, all they had to do was LISTEN. And so the months went by. A whole YEAR went by. And then, one day—

The pillar of cloud began to move! Everybody scurried this way and that. They packed up their tents and all their things. They packed dishes and rugs and clothes and blankets. But the most important thing to pack was the tent-church! They took down the curtains and the animal skins and carefully folded them. They packed the golden candlestick and the brass bowls and the table and the altar—everything! They unfastened the golden boards and put them in carts.

And last of all, they covered up the beautiful golden Ark with the angels on top. They covered it with the very special curtain that had been hanging inside the tent-church. Then they covered over that with badgers' skins. Then they covered over THAT with a blue, blue cloth. Then four men—hup—lifted it up and carried it very carefully on their shoulders. And then they listened.

And then—

The trumpets!

They blew a l-o-n-g "forward—MARCH!"

And everybody knew it was time to go! On they marched, through the wilderness. They knew that God was with them. For the pillar of cloud was there, and the trumpets were there—and all they had to do was STOP—LOOK—AND—LISTEN!

THINK!

Can you think of some of the signals in school that you have to obey in order to get along? How about at home? Which ones are you supposed to listen for? Which ones are you supposed to look for? What are the signals God gives us today, so we can follow him? What Book are these signals in?

A VERSE TO LEARN

Be ye therefore followers of God. (Ephesians 5:1)

LET'S PRAY

Dear God, sometimes signals and bells and things like that are a nuisance because they make us stop and do something when we'd rather be doing something else. Help us to remember that when we're obeying our parents and teachers and other people who are in authority over us,* we're really following GOD. And thank you for the Bible that tells us what you want us to do. In Jesus' name. Amen.

CAN YOU FIND THIS STORY IN THE BIBLE?

(Numbers 4: 1-33 and 9: 17-19 and 10: 1-36)

---

* People who are bosses over us.

You know how it is, when you're waiting for something wonderful to happen. Like your birthday. You wait and wait and WAIT—and you think it's NEVER going to come—and then, suddenly—there it is!

Two Against Ten

That's the way it was with the Hebrew people. Moses and the people marched and stopped and marched again and waited and WAITED. And then, suddenly—there it was! The Promised Land. Just a few miles away!

The pillar of cloud stopped. The people stopped. They put up their beautiful Tabernacle, and unpacked their things—and waited for God to tell them what to do. And he did.

"God has told me to send spies into the land," Moses told them.

Spies?

"Yes," said Moses, "I'm going to send twelve spies to

look over the land and come back and tell us what they saw."

Everyone talked at once. Spies—into the new land! It wouldn't be long now!

They talked about it while Moses chose twelve strong men to go. They talked about it while they gathered around the Tabernacle to ask God to be with them. They talked about it while the twelve men said good-by to their families and started off. And they were still talking about it when the men left, and disappeared—just specks in the distance. The Promised Land!

The people could hardly wait.

They looked and listened and talked about it. Ten days went by. What would the men find? Twenty days went by. How would they be treated? Thirty days went by. What would they have to tell when they got back? Thirty-five days went by. What if they DIDN'T come back? Ohhhhhhhh. Forty days went by. And then—

"They're coming, they're coming!" The shout went up all over the camp. And sure enough—first just specks in the distance—and then—the men—all twelve of them. They were safe! The people gathered around.

"There is fruit in the land," the spies said, and they swung a big pole off their shoulders with a bunch of grapes tied to it—nearly as big as a wheelbarrow! "There are figs and pomegranates too," they said, and they took fruit out of their packs such as the people had never seen before. "And there's grass—and water—and grain—everything!" they said—"BUT—!"

Everybody was quiet. Ten of the spies scowled. "We can't go," they said.

Can't go? The people's hearts almost stopped.

"We can't go over," the men went on. "The people are

strong and BIG—almost like GIANTS. And their cities have high walls that nearly reach to the sky. They'll kill us all. We can't go over!"

"Wait!"

It was the two other spies. Their names were Joshua and Caleb. "Wait!" they said, and they held up their hands. The people listened.

"We CAN go!" said Caleb. "God is with us. We needn't be afraid. Let's go!"

"No!" shouted the other spies.

"God will help us!" said Joshua and Caleb.

And the ten spies shouted and the people shouted, until you couldn't hear Joshua or Caleb at all.

"We can't go!" shouted the ten spies. And the people answered, "That's right! We can't go!"

And they didn't.

Those foolish people stayed in the wilderness. They stayed for years and YEARS. There was the Promised Land they'd been waiting for—but they didn't go over because they were afraid. And there was God, waiting to help them—but they didn't let him—because they didn't believe!

THINK!

How do you think YOU would have felt if you heard the spies say there were people like giants in the new land? Have you ever been afraid? When? Did you ask God to help you? How did God answer your prayer?

A VERSE TO LEARN

Fear thou not; for I am with thee: . . . I will help thee. (Isaiah 41:10)

LET'S PRAY

Dear God, we know it's not a sin to be afraid, but it IS a sin not to believe you will help us when you say you will. The whole idea is to ask you to give us the courage to do what is RIGHT. We thank you for your loving care. In Jesus' name. Amen.

CAN YOU FIND THIS STORY IN THE BIBLE?

(Numbers 13:1-33 and 14:1-45)

Jane was supposed to go to her aunt's right after her piano lesson. But she decided to go to her friend Paula's instead. Now Paula isn't home. And it's a long, long walk back. Paula's mother has already given Jane a glass of lemonade and sent her on her way.

But here sits Jane, sulking. Now she wishes she had gone where she was SUPPOSED to go. Because she did not, there's nothing but trouble, trouble, trouble. Such a dreary business!

More Grumble-Mumbles

No Promised Land! And all because the people didn't believe God could take care of them. The people of Israel turned back to the wilderness. And Moses turned sadly back with them.

God was still with them. The pillar of cloud was still there, and the tent-church was still there, and the manna was still there—but they weren't happy. They wandered from place to place in the wilderness, not getting anywhere, because they hadn't gone to the one place God had wanted them to go. And then—they got the mumble-grumbles again!

It started with LITTLE mumbles. "Nothing but manna, day after day," they mumbled to themselves. And they thought of the figs and other fruit and that big bunch of grapes on the pole. "Nothing but wilderness," they mumbled. And they thought of the grain and the trees and the big cities in the Promised Land. "Nothing but 'March—stop—march—stop!' " they thought, as they wandered around. And then they got to a place called Kadesh.

They were tired when they got to Kadesh and began to unpack and put up their tents. But that wasn't all. They were THIRSTY too. And there wasn't any water at Kadesh. That's when the little mumbles turned to BIG ones.

"Why did you bring us here?" they asked Moses. Mumble-grumble-mumble. "Why didn't you leave us in Egypt?" Mumble-grumble. "There is no fruit." Grumble-mumble. "And there is no grain." Mumble. "And now there isn't even any WATER!" Mumble-GRUMBLE.

Moses sighed. He was getting weary too. Weary of these people. And weary of their complaining. He knelt down and asked God what to do.

"Take your rod in your hand," God told Moses. "And gather all the people around that big rock over there. Then SPEAK to the rock, and it will give water."

Moses had the trumpeters blow on the long silver trumpets, and all the people gathered around. He stood up there by the rock and looked at them. He saw their scowling faces and heard their low mumble-grumbles—and suddenly—he was angry! He was angrier than he had ever been in his life!

"You—you REBELS!" he shouted. "Always wanting to have your own way. Must WE fetch water for you out of this rock?" And instead of SPEAKING to the rock, as God had told him to—Moses was so angry, he—

WHAM!

—took his rod and STRUCK the rock with all his might!

Oh—oh—OH. He'd said, "Must WE fetch water?" when it was GOD who was fetching the water. That was the worst thing he could have said. And he'd STRUCK the rock when God told him to SPEAK to it. That was the worst thing he could have done.

But, in a minute—

—the most wonderful thing happened!

Out of the rock—swirling, bubbling, foaming, tumbling —came—WATER! God had kept his promise!

The people cupped their hands and drank it. They filled their jugs with it. They splashed it over their faces and necks and arms.

WATER! It just kept coming out of that big rock. It kept coming and coming and COMING. Until there was enough for everybody.

But the people weren't very happy. Because they knew they had the grumble-mumbles in their hearts.

And Moses wasn't very happy, either. Because he knew that he had disobeyed God.

THINK!

God told Moses to do one thing and Moses did another. What was it? God sent the water all right but Moses still wasn't happy. Why? And the people weren't really happy either. Why? Can you think of a time when you were told to do one thing and you did another? How did it turn out? How did it make you feel?

A VERSE TO LEARN

If ye love me, keep my commandments. (John 14:15)

LET'S PRAY

Dear God, help us to remember that to obey means to do something EXACTLY as we are told—not just any old wishy-washy way. And keep us from the mumble-grumbles so we won't make everybody miserable. We thank you for loving us. In Jesus' name. Amen.

CAN YOU FIND THIS STORY IN THE BIBLE?

(Numbers 20:1-13)

The new Boys' Club is terrific. There sure are a lot of rules, though. Not just for the pool, either. There are signs with rules for the baseball diamond and for the club house and even the tennis courts. There are even rules saying that boys of certain ages can use the club only during certain hours. The boys really can't find fault with the rules, though. Every single one is for their own good. And they're so happy to HAVE the club—it's EASY to obey the rules—cheerfully!

The Laws That Lasted Forever

Now a lot of important things happened to Moses and his people as they wandered through the wilderness, but one of the most IMPORTANT things, was what happened in this story.

It was BEFORE the spies went into the Promised Land. And before Moses whammed the rock.

Do you remember way back when Moses came down from that huge mountain* and told the people God wanted them to build a tent-church? Well, God wanted them to do something else, too. And this is what it was.

"You know how good God has been to us," said Moses. "He has helped us every time we've been in trouble. NOW—"

* Mount Sinai

"Now—WHAT?" the people wondered.

"NOW—" said Moses, "he wants US to do something for HIM. He wants us to belong to him in a VERY SPECIAL way. And he wants to give us a SET OF LAWS —so we will know how he wants us to live. And you may have your CHOICE. Do you want these laws or not?"

Did they want the laws? Oh YES! "Tell God we'll do anything he says!" they cried.

So Moses went back up the mountain to tell God. And when he came back down he had something even MORE IMPORTANT to say. "You must get all cleaned up," he said, "and wash your clothes. For in three days God is coming right to the mountain. He'll be RIGHT HERE."

Oh MY!

Everybody got busy at once. They cleaned the camp. They washed their clothes. They washed themselves. And then they waited. And sure enough—

On the morning of the third day, suddenly—

The lightning FLASHED!

The thunder CRASHED!

A mysterious trumpet BLEW!

And the mountain SHOOK!

And SMOKED!

And TREMBLED!

The people trembled too. They backed up and BACKED UP—until they were a safe distance away. And there they waited—frightened.

But Moses went right up into the mountain and INTO THE SMOKE, to get the set of laws from God. And when he came back—

Sure enough, he told them all the laws God wanted them to obey. "We will obey!" they shouted. "All that God says we will obey!"

And do you know, those laws have lasted right up until today—for they are the TEN COMMANDMENTS we have in the Bible! They are lasting forever—or at least until Jesus comes back again!

THINK!

Does God give us rules and laws to make us miserable? Think of some commands God has given us in the Bible. Then think about why he gave them. What are some rules you have at home? At school? At church? If you love God, what will you do about rules and laws and commandments?

A VERSE TO LEARN

The law of the LORD is perfect. (Psalm 19:7)

LET'S PRAY

Dear God, you are so good to us! One of the most wonderful things you do for us is to give us rules and laws to obey for our own good. Help us to obey cheerfully. In Jesus' name. Amen.

CAN YOU FIND THIS STORY IN THE BIBLE?

(Exodus, chapter 19)

CAN YOU FIND THE TEN COMMANDMENTS IN THE BIBLE?

(Exodus 20:1-17)

PART 4   STORIES OF JESUS

The most important thing in the world for Roy and Tammy these days, is getting home to see what the mailman has left. For their Uncle Jack has gone away across the ocean to another country. And he's promised to send them some gifts! Oh joy! Such a mystery! What'll they be? Costumed dolls? A shepherd's flute? A string of wooden camels? A bow and arrow? It will be something WONDERFUL for sure. And it will come ONE of these days, for Uncle Jack always keeps his promises.

The Greatest Promise in the World

Once a long, long time ago, the greatest gift in the WORLD was promised. Can you imagine a gift so great and so important that it changed the whole world?

Well, there was a gift just that important. It was a gift God had promised to send to the world.

It wasn't a palace.

It wasn't gold.

It was—A BABY!

A very special baby—God's own son, the baby Jesus.

It was promised to a young woman named Mary. And to a kind man named Joseph. And this is how it all happened.

Mary and Joseph lived in Bible times when angels sometimes spoke to people. They don't NOW. But they did THEN.

And one day Mary was praying to God. She didn't know there was going to be a gift. She didn't expect an angel. She didn't even expect a PROMISE. But SUDDENLY—

An angel! Right there before her eyes!

Mary was frightened. She'd never SEEN an angel before. And this angel was SPEAKING to her!

"Don't be afraid, Mary," the angel said. "God loves you very much. You are going to be the mother of a dear baby boy. He'll be God's own son. And his name will be Jesus."

And then the angel was gone. Just like that!

Mary stayed there and thought and thought. This was a most wonderful promise. GOD made this promise. And when GOD makes a promise, he always keeps it. Why, this would be the greatest gift in the world!

Then one night while Joseph was sleeping, HE saw an angel too! And the angel told him all about Mary and the wonderful promise.

O joy!

"I'm going to be the mother of a baby boy," Mary thought as she made some blankets to keep him warm. "He will be God's son," she thought as she made clothes for him to wear. "His name will be Jesus," she thought as she fixed a bed for him to sleep in.

So Mary and Joseph got ready for the wonderful gift. For they knew it was coming. They had seen an ANGEL. God had promised it. And God always keeps his promises.

The world didn't know it yet, but Jesus was coming! He was coming all right! For he'd been PROMISED!

THINK!

Can you find these promises in the Bible? Genesis 28:15; Jeremiah 33:3; Psalm 121:3; Isaiah 41:10; Romans 8:28; Philippians 4:19.

God's promise to send his son was the most wonderful promise of all. Do you know why? (See p. 12, Story 3)

Aren't you glad God always keeps his promises? How can you thank him for this?

A VERSE TO LEARN

There hath not failed one word of all his good promise. (I Kings 8:56)

LET'S PRAY

Dear God, we're certainly glad to know that when you make a promise you always keep it. Help us to remember this and to believe you. And help us to keep OUR promises too! In Jesus' name. Amen.

CAN YOU FIND THIS STORY IN THE BIBLE?

(Luke 1:26-38 and Matthew 1:18-25)

Carol and Ted are waving good-by to mother. She's on her way to the hospital. And they can hardly wait until she gets back home again. For she's going to bring back a baby! Woooeeee! A real live one! He'll kick and cry and smile and blow bubbles and maybe some day even dump his cereal all over his head. Or maybe he'll even be a girl. Whatever, having a new baby in the house is always lots of fun.

The Promise Comes True

God had made Mary and Joseph a promise. Not an ordinary promise. It was an EARTH-SHAKING promise. He promised them a very special baby—God's own son, the baby Jesus.

Imagine!

Of course, Mary should go to the very best hospital or maybe even a king's palace for this very special baby to be born. Or stay home and have servants and nurses hurrying and scurrying about, carrying trays and orange juice and sheets and medicine and bumping into each other. And with maids to comb her hair and bathe the new baby and dress him in the finest clothing and brush what little hair he had up to a curl on top and carry him to her bedside and put him gently alongside her, with his tiny head snuggled in the pillow—

But none of this happened at all.

What really happened is quite amazing.

It all began with the king's order. It tells us in the Bible— "...there went out a decree from Caesar Augustus, that all the world should be taxed...and all went to be taxed, every one into his own city." Which simply meant that Joseph and Mary had to pack up a few belongings on a little donkey, leave their comfortable little house in Nazareth, and clump along bumpy roads—all the way to Bethlehem to pay their taxes and sign the king's book!

Then there was the matter of the crowds. When they finally got to Bethlehem it was just SPILLING OVER with people who had also come to pay their taxes. People and donkeys and camels and bundles and food and sheep and goats—you just can't IMAGINE the confusion!

And then there was the matter of a place to stay. And THAT was the worst part. For there WAS no place to stay. The inns* were filled. EVERY place that had rooms to rent was filled. And poor Mary and Joseph went all over Bethlehem, knocking on doors and getting turned away and knocking on doors and getting turned away until—

One innkeeper said, "Wait!" He had just thought of something. And what he thought of was not nice beds and clean sheets and a warm bath. It was a STABLE—where the cattle slept! And that is where Mary and Joseph finally went. And that was where, that very night, God's promise came true—and the baby Jesus was born. In-

---

* An inn' is like a motel only instead of having cars, the people had donkeys or camels to park out in a stable.

144

stead of clean sheets there was straw and instead of servants and nurses and doctors there were donkeys and sheep and cows sleeping.

Yes, there baby Jesus was born. And there, Mary wrapped him in soft clean cloth and laid him—oh so carefully—on some clean straw, in a manger.*

It might SEEM that everything had gone wrong. But actually everything had gone exactly as God wanted it to go.

Jesus had been promised. And now he was HERE!

THINK!

Just imagine how different the world would be if God hadn't kept his promise. Can you think of some ways in which it would be different? Can you think of some ways you can thank God for keeping this great promise?

A VERSE TO LEARN

He [God] *loved us, and sent his Son.* (I John 4:10)

LET'S PRAY

Dear God, we thank you that you loved us so much that you sent us the Lord Jesus to be our Saviour. It sure was a great promise and we're glad you kept it. In Jesus' name. Amen.

CAN YOU FIND THIS STORY IN THE BIBLE?

(Luke 2:1-7)

---

* A manger is a long box to hold the animals' food.

When new babies are born—how do people find out about it? On the phone? In an announcement card? Or a letter? Do people call it out from their front porch? Clearly, the very FIRST thing to do is to let everybody know, one way or the other—and as soon as possible!

"A baby!"

"Really?"

"Yes—a boy!"

"How big?"

"Eight and a half pounds!"

"My a BIG fellow! How wonderful!"

It's just too important to keep secret!

The Strangest Announcement in the World

When Jesus was born, there were no announcement cards sent out. But people found out about it in the strangest ways!

There were some people who lived nearby who found out about it. They were shepherds. And they found out about it in the middle of the night. And this is how it happened.

They were watching their sheep on a hillside. Everything was so quiet you could hear a blade of grass if it twittered in the breeze. Once in awhile, a baby lamb would wake up and go "Baaaaa"—but its mother would lick its ears and say "Shhhhhhhh"—and it would go back to sleep. Then everything would be quiet again. Then suddenly—

There was an ANGEL—right before their eyes! And a bright, BRIGHT light—right in the sky!

The shepherds couldn't believe their eyes. They looked at the angel. And at the bright light. And at each other. And they were afraid.

"Don't be afraid," the angel said. "I have good news! A Saviour* has just been born. He is in Bethlehem right this minute. Lying in a manger."

"The Saviour! Oh joy! Could it be TRUE?"

Just then the sky was FULL of angels. And they were saying, "Glory to God in the highest, and on earth peace, good will toward men."

And then, suddenly—

The angels were gone.

And the bright light was gone.

And it was dark again.

The shepherds looked at each other. It MUST be true! They would GO to Bethlehem and find out. And they DID.

They stumbled across the fields and puffed up the hills and sneaked through the streets. And then—

They came to a stable. They looked in the doorway. And there was Mary. There was Joseph. There were sheep. And goats. And cows. There was a manger with hay in it. And there—all snuggled in the straw—was baby Jesus!

---

* The Saviour is the Lord Jesus.

It was true!

Shhhh. They went in quietly. And shhh. They knelt down. And shhh. They thanked God for baby Jesus.

And then they went back to their sheep.

Oh, they were happy! For they had found out about the most important baby that had ever been born. Not by telephone. Not by an announcement card. Not by a letter. But by ANGELS—and a light in the sky!

For this was not just ANY baby. This was God's Son.

THINK!

Can you think of other ways God might have announced that Jesus was born? Why do you suppose he chose this way? How can you help other people know the good news that God sent his Son to be our Saviour?

A VERSE TO LEARN

For unto you is born this day in the city of David* a Saviour, which is Christ the Lord. (Luke 2:11)

LET'S PRAY

Dear God, first you made a promise and then you kept it and then you TOLD people about it. We certainly thank you for all this. Help us to remember that it's important to tell people about that promise and all about how you kept it and everything. In Jesus' name. Amen.

CAN YOU FIND THIS STORY IN THE BIBLE?

(Luke 2:8-20)

* Bethlehem

When new babies are born, how do people find out about it when they live far away? Laurie and Jeff have a brand new baby brother. And they've let everybody know by announcements and cards and phone calls. But grandma and grandpa live way across the ocean in another country and there is only one way to let them know. By a CABLEGRAM! First dad has to write the message on a special paper, then the telegraph company has to phone the message way across the ocean, then it has to be written down again on ANOTHER special paper, then at LAST grandpa and grandma read it. Such a business!

Two Dreams That Saved a Little Child

Yes, people found out about the birth of Jesus in strange ways. There were people who lived near by who found out about it. They were shepherds. And there were people who lived far away who found out about it. They were wise men who lived in another country. And when THEY found out about it, they did something that nearly caused baby Jesus harm—DREADFUL harm. It happened this way.

These wise men studied the stars. They knew that God had promised to send a Saviour-King.* One night they saw a HUGE star, brighter than all the rest. And they knew it must be the star that would tell them where the Saviour-King was.

So they packed some gifts and got on their camels and followed that star right to Bethlehem. And they went straight to the palace where King Herod lived.

"We have followed God's star," they told King Herod. "We are looking for the new King God promised."

King Herod was very polite and asked them all about the star.

"The child is not here," said King Herod. "But when you find him, let me know where he is. I would like to worship him, too." And he sent them on their way to Bethlehem.

The wise men went on to look for Jesus. But they didn't know one thing—

Herod was a WICKED king. And he didn't want to find Jesus to WORSHIP him. He wanted to KILL him!

When the wise men came to where Mary and Joseph and little Jesus were, they unpacked their camels and brought out the finest gifts of gold and rare perfumes. And they knelt down and worshiped Jesus. Then they got ready to go back and tell the wicked king where Jesus was. And they would have told him, and Jesus might have been KILLED—except for one thing.

God was watching!

That night in a dream, God told the wise men, "Do not

* This was baby Jesus.

150

go back to wicked King Herod. He doesn't want to worship Jesus. He wants to have him KILLED. Go back to your own country."

And the wise men did!

But King Herod was angry. He called his soldiers. "Go to Bethlehem," he told them, "and find this child—I want to have him killed!"

But God was still watching!

At night, in a dream, God told Joseph to take Mary and Jesus and run away. Mary and Joseph packed up their things and wrapped up little Jesus, and stole out of the city and across the desert until they got to Egypt, a country far away.

And when the soldiers got to Bethlehem and looked in all the places where there were little children so they could kill baby Jesus—he was gone!

King Herod never found Jesus. And Mary and Joseph didn't bring him back until the wicked king was dead.

No harm could come to God's son. Because God was watching!

THINK!

Phew! That was close, wasn't it? They didn't have cablegrams and telegrams and phones back in those days, but God used other ways to announce Jesus' birth, and other ways to SAVE Jesus when his life was in danger. What were they? What are some ways God protects YOU from danger?

A VERSE TO LEARN

The LORD is thy keeper. (Psalm 121:5)

LET'S PRAY

Dear God, we thank you for taking such good care of Jesus and for letting the wise men know about him and then we thank you ESPECIALLY for not letting that wicked King Herod go and spoil it all. We thank you for giving us parents and teachers and policemen and all sorts of people to keep us safe. In Jesus' name. Amen.

CAN YOU FIND THIS STORY IN THE BIBLE?

(Matthew 2:1-23)

Dick is looking at his baby brother in DISMAY.* Small children are supposed to do stupid things, but honestly, this is RIDICULOUS! What Dick doesn't realize is that in order to grow up and learn, children have to touch things, put things in their mouths, break things, spill things, and try out all sorts of new ideas, like dumping cereal on their heads. And what Dick doesn't REMEMBER is that HE dumped a bowl of pudding over HIS head once! He had to learn too. Now he swings a baseball bat. But he had to learn to swing a rattle first.

When Jesus Was a Little Boy

Even though Jesus was God's own son, he had to grow up just like any other little boy. And God was watching over him every minute.

* That means "I give up!"

After the wicked King Herod was dead, and Mary and Joseph and Jesus came back from Egypt—they went to Nazareth to live. Nazareth wasn't a great big city with tall buildings and temples and lots of traffic. It was a little country town, tucked away in the hills.

By this time Jesus wasn't a baby any longer—he was a little boy!

The Bible tells us that he had to learn things. And that he obeyed his mother and Joseph. And that Joseph was a carpenter. So we have a pretty good idea of what Jesus' life was like.

In the morning, the sunshine would sneak in Jesus' window and across his bedroom floor and up the side of his bed and over the top of his covers—and in his eyes—and wake him. Mary would pour water in a basin and help Jesus get washed and dressed. And then it was time for breakfast.

While Mary got breakfast, Jesus would put the dishes on the low bench they used for a table and spread the mats on the floor for them to sit on. Then Mary and Joseph and Jesus sat around on the mats, and Joseph would thank God for their breakfast while they all bowed their heads. Then they would eat barley cakes with fresh butter and honey. And while they ate, they would talk about what they were going to do that day and ask God to help them do everything just right.

There were so many things to do INSIDE their house.

And Jesus helped with everything. He helped feed the animals. He helped Mary get water at the well. And he helped Joseph, too.

He helped Joseph in his carpenter shop. He handed Joseph nails and pieces of wood. He caught the curly shavings as they fell to the floor. And he watched the sawdust sprinkle the floor, like snow, when Joseph went szhhh-szhhh with the saw. And Jesus obeyed Mary and Joseph in everything they asked him to do.

There were so many things to do OUTSIDE their house.

There were walks in the hills and rides on the donkey, and picnics, and friends to play with.

And in the evening Mary and Joseph and Jesus would sit on their doorstep and watch the sun go down—and talk about God. They would tell God's stories over and over, until Jesus knew them all by heart.

And then Jesus would say his prayers and go to bed. And the stars came out—and all of Nazareth would go to sleep, tucked away there in the hills.

That's the way the other people in Nazareth lived. And that's the way Jesus lived, too.

Even though he was God's Son, he had to grow up just like any other little boy.

And God was watching over him every minute.

THINK!

What were some of the things Jesus found to do inside his house? Outside? What do you suppose he learned when he helped Joseph and Mary? When he played with his friends? When he went on hikes? When he rode a donkey? When he took care of animals? Do you learn just about the same things today?

A VERSE TO LEARN

Children, obey your parents in the Lord: for this is right. (Ephesians 6:1)

LET'S PRAY

Dear God, help us to remember that in everything we do, we are learning something. We learn to be good sports and to be helpful and to obey and to use our muscles when we hike and play outside. Thank you that learning is FUN most of the time, and help us to be good sports when it ISN'T fun. In Jesus' name. Amen.

CAN YOU FIND THIS STORY IN THE BIBLE?

(Luke 2:40 and 52)

Melissa is getting the hem of her dress let down AGAIN. And though it's a dreary bore to stand still so long, she is secretly proud that she is GROWING. It's Fred's turn next and while he's waiting he's checking up on how tall he is. Another inch! Such a business! He's so proud he's growing, he feels like CROWING. He acts as if he invented growing himself. Of course we all know that without God, we wouldn't grow an inch!

When Jesus Was a Big Boy

Remember the very first day Mother took you to school? She marched you into the building and up the hall, right into Miss Chalk-dust's room. She introduced you to your teacher and whispered something in your ear about using your handkerchief instead of your sleeve— and then she went HOME—and you were on your own! Oh, joy! Oh, HORRORS! You were half-glad and half-scared. It was all so new! And then, after a while, you got used to it. Remember?

Well, Jesus had to go to school, too. While he was busy helping Mary and Joseph, and learning to obey—he was

GROWING. And before he knew it, it was time for him to start going to school.

NOW, things were different. In the morning, when the first rays of the sun s-t-r-e-t-c-h-e-d across his bedcovers and got to his face to wake him, it was more important to get up than ever before.

School!

Jesus washed and dressed himself. Mary didn't help him with these things any more. Jesus spent some time by himself, talking alone with his heavenly Father.

The chores had to be done quickly now. Jesus fed his pets and set the table—and now that he was bigger, perhaps Joseph let HIM thank God for their breakfast!

There wasn't any Miss Chalk-dust, and school wasn't a big building with lots of rooms and desks. The teacher was the MINISTER, and school was in the SYNAGOGUE.* And everything was different. Jesus had to get used to it, the same as you had to get used to your school. He sat on the floor, cross-legged, along with the other boys, and learned.

Jesus learned God's Word. He learned to read from a long strip of paper with a stick at each end. He u-n-r-o-l-l-e-d it and read it, and r-o-l-l-e-d it up again on the other stick. It was called a scroll.

Jesus listened to everything the teacher said, and then said it over and OVER until he knew it by heart. There was so much to learn!

Some things were easy. Some things were hard, and Jesus bowed his head and asked God to help him.

And when he got home, he told Mary all the new things he had learned.

And when Mary and Joseph and Jesus sat on their doorstep in the evening, to watch the sun go down, some-

* A synagogue is a place of worship just as your church is.

158

times Joseph let HIM tell the Bible story.

Oh, yes, things were different now.

Everything was more exciting. Everything was more important. Even though Jesus was God's own Son, he went to school and LEARNED things. Just like any other boy!

THINK!

What are some of the things Jesus could do for himself now, that Mary used to help him with? What was the most important thing he learned at school? What are some of the things YOU do for yourself now that you used to have help with? Think about some of the NEW things you've learned in just the past year. Doesn't it make you feel OLD?

A VERSE TO LEARN

I will not forget thy word. (Psalm 119:16)

LET'S PRAY

Dear God, Jesus certainly must love us, to come to earth as a baby and grow up and have to LEARN just like anybody else. If he did all these things then he must understand EXACTLY how WE feel. That's a pretty wonderful thing to know when we get discouraged. Thank you a lot, Lord. In Jesus' name. Amen.

CAN YOU FIND THIS STORY IN THE BIBLE?

(Luke 2:40 and 46 and 47 and 52)

Alice is in church. And her mind isn't on the singing. But her mind IS on Jesus. She's thinking about how he had to go to school and learn and grow up and everything. But his REAL job was "to be about his father's business." And his father was God! Jesus had some work to do for his father. And he never forgot it, even when he was a boy.

Lost: One Boy

Jesus could hardly wait until he was twelve years old. Because when he was twelve years old, something VERY IMPORTANT was going to happen. He was going to go with Mary and Joseph to the big temple in Jerusalem! Every year, fathers and mothers traveled to the big temple to worship—but boys couldn't go to the temple services until they were twelve.

All his life, Jesus thought about the wonderful day when he would be allowed to go. And at last he was twelve!

Oh, joy! Such scrubbing and packing and cooking to get ready! What a golden day it was, when Mary and Joseph and Jesus started out, with their little donkey packed right up to his long ears. What fun to meet other families along the way and travel along together. There were donkeys and camels and carts to carry things and people. There were goats and sheep and turtledoves and cattle to give to God. There were days of traveling. And finally—

JERUSALEM!

Jerusalem—with its funny, crooked cobblestone streets and rows of stores right outdoors. And the TEMPLE!

They could see its golden roof from a distance. They went through its big gates and into the huge courts. Of course, they could not go into the INNER courts. They could not see the rich curtains of red and blue and purple —and great chests made of brass—and candlesticks made of gold. But they went each day to worship God. And at last it was time to go back to Nazareth.

Mary and Joseph thought Jesus was with them when they started across the hills with the crowd. But when they stopped in the evening to rest, they looked for him— and he was GONE!

How dreadful! They went through the crowds, asking everybody. Nobody had seen him. Mary and Joseph went back to Jerusalem again, and for three days they looked in the streets, in the homes of their friends—everywhere. Then they looked in the temple—

And there he was!

Not playing. Not crying. But sitting with the wise men of the temple, talking about the things of God! Jesus was answering the questions of the wise men, and they were surprised at how much he knew.

"Why have you done this, my son?" Mary asked him. "We've been looking for you everywhere."

"You didn't look in the right place," said Jesus. "Didn't you know I'd be here about my Father's business?"

They went back home to Nazareth, and the days went on exactly as they had before.

But Jesus had given Mary and Joseph quite a jolt. He reminded them of WHO HE WAS. They never forgot that day, when Jesus was twelve years old. And they never forgot that Jesus is really God's own Son.

THINK!

This was the first time Jesus ever acted as if he were really God's Son. How do you suppose it made Mary and Joseph feel? What did the inside of the temple look like? Do you know what his "Father's business" was? (Look back to story 33.) How do you think Jesus felt about God's house?

A VERSE TO LEARN

I was glad when they said unto me, Let us go into the house of the LORD. (Psalm 122:1)

LET'S PRAY

Dear God, we thank you for sending Jesus to earth to die for us and rise again into heaven so we could be with him there some day. We thank you that you made him a baby and a boy and all the rest, because that helps us to understand him better, and we know he understands us and how we feel. In Jesus' name. Amen.

CAN YOU FIND THIS STORY IN THE BIBLE?

(Luke 2:40-52)

This is one of the most EXCITING days in Jimmy's life. He couldn't even SLEEP last night. For today his dad promised to take him to the airport to get a peek at the PRESIDENT OF THE UNITED STATES! Jimmy never dreamed the President would see him because he was down so low, but joy of joys! And surprise of surprises! The President DID see him, and stooped way over to shake hands! Now Jimmy won't be able to sleep tonight either! Phew!

The Children Find a Friend

The day the wonderful news came, the little town by the lake was turned upside down with excitement, and nothing was ever quite the same again. The news was—well it was so exciting that it spread like wildfire!

The children heard it in the streets, and they ran into

their houses, falling over pet lambs and sending pigeons flying in every direction.

"Mother! Jesus is here!"

And their mothers stopped mixing the bread dough and said, "Jesus? Where?"

"Here, Mother. HERE. He's on his way to Jerusalem, and he's stopping here and he has his helpers with him, and—"

But their mothers had already rinsed their hands and dried them on their aprons.

"Jesus is here!" they cried. "Go get your father!"

And so the news spread, until everybody knew about it, and the fishing was forgotten and the shops were closed. Everybody wanted to see Jesus. The mothers especially wanted Jesus to bless their children.

Perhaps if they hurried and got there early, they could see him. The children stuck close to their mothers, and they all talked at once as they hurried to the place where Jesus was.

But when they got there, the most DREADFUL of all things happened. They couldn't even get near him!

The mothers tried to get through the crowd. The children tried to squiggle through. But they couldn't.

The mothers thought perhaps if they spoke to Jesus' disciples, THEN they could see him. "Please—" they began, "We wondered if perhaps—"

"What do you want here?" the disciples said. Well, that wasn't a very good beginning. But the mothers grew bolder.

"We want Jesus to bless our children!" they cried. And the disciples said, "Go away. Jesus isn't interested in children."

Well. That was that. The mothers and children turned

sadly away. It was no use. But then—That WASN'T that!

"Don't turn the children away," said a voice. Who was that? Who was THAT? They listened hard. "Bring them here to me," the voice went on. It was JESUS! Oh, joy!

Could it be true?

It WAS! The crowd was separating to let them through!

The children started to walk toward Jesus, slowly. Then they walked faster. Then they RAN. They ran right up to him and stood around him, by his knee—and he put his hand on their heads and blessed them. Oh, it was wonderful. It was better than they had dared dream!

They all went home happy. And on evenings when they sat in their doorways, they had something to talk about for years.

The little town was never quite the same again. Jesus had stopped there.

The fathers and mothers were never quite the same again. For they had SEEN him.

And the children were never quite the same again. For they had TOUCHED him!

THINK!

Do you think Jesus cares just as much about children today? What are some things in your life that make you think that Jesus cares about you? What has God given you to READ so you'll know Jesus cares about you personally?

A VERSE TO LEARN

We love him, because he first loved us. (I John 4:19)

LET'S PRAY

Dear God, you have loved us for a long long time, even before we knew you. And you love us today. You tell us in the Bible. And you let us know by all the things you do for us. We thank you for your great love. Help us to love you back even better than ever before. In Jesus' name. Amen.

CAN YOU FIND THIS STORY IN THE BIBLE?

(Matthew 19:13-15 and Mark 10:13-16 and Luke 18:15-17)

Joy is sick. And the joy around the house is GONE. Because Joy is sick enough to have a doctor. He's a good doctor and his pills are just beautiful—the gayest colors you can imagine. And some of them are so good to taste you can even CHEW them. But Joy and her mother and father are asking God to watch over her, too!

The Boy the Doctors Couldn't Cure

The beautiful house in Capernaum was quiet. The nobleman who lived there was brokenhearted. His little boy was very, very sick.

"There is nothing we can do for him," said the doctors. And they shook their heads.

"Nothing to do—nothing to do—" thought the nobleman, as he stood by his son's bed. "Nothing, unless—"

Then he suddenly thought of something! Jesus was in the town of Cana! The nobleman had heard his friends telling wonderful tales of how Jesus was teaching, and curing the sick—

"Get my horse ready," the nobleman said to his servants. "I'm going to Cana!"

The servants hurried to obey, and as the nobleman left, he said, "Take care of my son. I'm going to bring Jesus back with me!" And off he went to Cana as fast as he could go.

It was about one o'clock when the nobleman got to Cana. When he saw the crowds, his heart sank. "Jesus will be too busy to come," he thought, as he pushed his way through the crowd. "He won't be able to come, and my son will die," he thought, as he struggled to get up close to where Jesus was. By the time he got to Jesus, the nobleman was almost crying.

"Please, Jesus!" he said. "Come to Capernaum and heal my son!"

Jesus looked at the nobleman, with the kindest eyes in the world. Jesus didn't say he would come. He didn't say he WOULDN'T come. He said something far more wonderful. He simply said, "Go back home. Your son is better."

And suddenly, in his heart, the nobleman KNEW that his son was better. He thanked Jesus, and went back through the crowds, and started for home. All his fear was gone. He knew Jesus meant what he said.

All the way home he thought about it. And as he got near his house—

Servants from his house—running to meet him! "Your son did not die!" they cried. "He is well!"

"I know—I know!" said the nobleman. "Jesus healed him!" And they all started back for the house.

"Just when," asked the nobleman on the way back to the house, "did my son start to get better?"

"About one o'clock," they cried. "Yes—it was just one o'clock."

"Ahhh," he said quietly, "that is just what I expected

you to say. For that is just the hour Jesus said to me, 'Go back home—your son is better.'"

And they bowed their heads then and there and thanked God.

And oh—the house in Capernaum was bright again! And the nobleman was happy. Jesus had healed his son without even seeing him. Nobody else could do that.

But Jesus could. He is the Son of God.

THINK!

Actually we have doctors to help make us well. But who do you suppose helps the doctors? Do you think it's right to ask God to make us better when we have doctors? Why?

A VERSE TO LEARN

He healed many that were sick. (Mark 1:34)

LET'S PRAY

Dear God, we thank you that you care about us when we're sick. And we know that you can help the doctors make us better, and sometimes you even help us when the doctors CAN'T. We love you. In Jesus' name. Amen.

CAN YOU FIND THIS STORY IN THE BIBLE?

(John 4:46-53)

It's Blind Man's Bluff, and Arnie is "it." How strange everything is behind that dark bandage! Arnie can't see a thing and he can't tell WHICH way he is going. The other children are supposed to keep quiet so he won't know where they are, but he has just bumped into a chair and it was so FUNNY they laughed before they remembered. Such fun! But Arnie is "blind" for only a few minutes. If he were REALLY blind all the time—it wouldn't be funny at all.

The Man Who Couldn't See

Bartimaeus was blind, and there wasn't a chance in the world that he would ever see. He lived in Jericho, but he never saw the gardens and palm trees and market places. He sat by the side of the street and begged for money, but he never saw the crowds that went by or the people who stopped to give him a few pennies. He lived in a world of

BLACKNESS. And nobody seemed to care.

One day, Bartimaeus felt his way along the streets until he came to the big city gate. He sat down against the wall and began to beg. The people hurried by. He heard the clop-clop of the donkeys. Some sheep passed by so close he could touch their woolly sides. It was just like any other day. And then—

There was a sudden excitement in the air. He could FEEL it. People scrambled off to the side of the road. They backed up until they crowded against him. Everybody was talking at once.

"What is it?" cried Bartimaeus. "What's going on?" And he listened HARD to the voices around him.

"It's Jesus!"

"He's on his way to Jerusalem!"

"Out of the way, there. Back up!"

"There he is now!"

Oh, yes—Jesus. Bartimaeus could understand the excitement. No wonder! People followed Jesus everywhere. He taught them, and healed them—

He HEALED them—

Suddenly Bartimaeus' heart did a flip-flop. A great wild hope zoomed up inside of him. "Jesus—have mercy on me!" he shouted.

"Be quiet!" the people told him. "Stop shouting."

But Bartimaeus didn't stop. "Jesus—help me!" he cried, and he scrambled to his feet. And then—

Everyone grew quiet. Jesus had stopped, right in the middle of the road. He said something to his disciples. Bartimaeus could hear people mumbling. Then he could feel them jostling, moving sideways. He listened HARD. And then someone called, "Jesus wants to talk to you."

Bartimaeus could hardly believe it! He threw off his

coat and he started to move forward. Then somebody took his arm. And the next thing he knew—

"What is it you want me to do for you?" It was the kindest voice. It was Jesus!

"Lord, that I might receive my sight!" said Bartimaeus through the blackness. And then—Jesus spoke softly—

"Because you believe that I can do this for you, you shall see."

The blackness rolled away like a cloud. And there before Bartimaeus' eyes—stood Jesus! Bartimaeus could SEE him. And all around him—

men and women
and bright-colored robes
and the city gates—

oh, so many things, Bartimaeus didn't know where to look first! It was a great ocean of color! Then he looked back at Jesus. He said "thank you" to Jesus in every way he could think of. And when Jesus turned to walk down the road, Bartimaeus followed along with the crowd. He forgot how he had planned to spend the day. He forgot EVERY-THING—except that he loved Jesus—and that he could SEE.

Bartimaeus had been blind. And there wasn't a chance in the world that he would ever see—until Jesus came along. Now he could see everything—like an ocean of color. But best of all—he could see JESUS.

THINK!

Think of some of the wonderful things you see every day. Can you name a few of them? And how about all the things you learn. Could you learn as fast if you couldn't see? And what if you couldn't see your friends? Would you like them as much? But supposing you really COULDN'T see. Do you remember the story of Fanny Crosby in Story 17. Did Fanny decide to sulk? What did she wind up doing? Do you think she had a happy life?

A VERSE TO LEARN

Jesus of Nazareth . . . went about doing good. (Acts 10:38)

LET'S PRAY

Dear God, we certainly do thank you for all the beautiful things we can see around us. (Thank him for some of the special things you can see.) And we thank you for Fanny Crosby who couldn't see, but who obeyed instead of sulking. In Jesus' name. Amen.

CAN YOU FIND THIS STORY IN THE BIBLE?

(Mark 10:46-52 and Luke 18:35-43)

Well, here they are on the picnic and the new girl forgot her lunch. Such a business! Kim looks at her own lunch, which really isn't too big. And she thinks, "Well, some of the ladies in charge will give her something." And THEN she thinks, "Well OF COURSE I'm supposed to share my things. What have I been waiting for?" And she offers the new girl a sandwich. And do you know, this is going to make Kim feel so good that later on she will offer to share her potato chips and cake and apple too?

The Most Extraordinary Lunch in the World

Back in the land where Jesus lived, an ordinary boy started off on an ordinary hike, on an ordinary day. He didn't know it, but it was going to be the most important day in his life! His mother gave him an ordinary lunch. Oh, it was a VERY ordinary lunch. Five barley loaves and two little dried fishes!

He whistled along the hills and up and down the paths. He whistled his way clear down to the shores of Lake Galilee.

Then he stopped.

There was a bigger crowd of people than he had ever seen before—more than five thousand people! They weren't standing. They seemed to be GOING someplace. And being filled with an ordinary amount of curiosity, he asked where they were going.

"See that boat?" they said.

Sure enough, there was a boat in the middle of the lake, going toward the other side.

"Jesus is in that boat. We're going to the other side of the lake so we can be there when he lands!"

Jesus!

The boy didn't stop a minute. He whistled his way right along with the crowd so he could be there, too.

When Jesus and his disciples landed on the other side of the lake, the crowd grew very quiet. Jesus began to tell them stories. The boy stopped whistling and got way up front so he wouldn't miss a thing. He listened through the afternoon. He was still listening as the long shadows began to tuck the hills in bed.

Then one of the disciples said to Jesus, "Send these people home. It is time for them to get bread for themselves, for they have nothing to eat."

And Jesus said, "Where can we buy bread?"

"Why, Master," they told him, "if we took a man's paycheck for a WHOLE MONTH and spent it ALL on bread, there wouldn't be enough. Send them home."

But Jesus said, "No. Give them something to eat. How much bread do you have? Go and see."

The disciples started toward the crowd. The boy pricked up his ears. "I have my lunch!" he shouted. Just like that. He held it up—and before you could say, "five barley loaves," a disciple had led him right up to Jesus! The boy gave his lunch to Jesus. Then he watched hard. Everybody sat down in groups and watched hard.

Jesus bowed his head and thanked God for the lunch. Then he began to break the barley loaves and fishes in pieces. And then a wonderful thing began to happen. The more pieces Jesus broke off, the more pieces were left! The disciples began to pass them out, walking between the groups of people. And when the disciples came back, there were MORE pieces. There were just pieces and pieces and PIECES. Even after everyone was fed there was enough left to fill—twelve baskets!

The boy looked at what was left over from his ordinary lunch. It was hard to believe. He had started out on an ordinary hike on an ordinary day. It had started out just like any other day. But it turned out to be the most important day of his life.

Nothing was very ORDINARY when Jesus was around!

THINK!

Just imagine sitting on a hillside listening to JESUS tell stories! What are some things Jesus might have taught the people about God? How do you suppose the boy felt about sharing his lunch? What do you think he thought about before he shouted out that he had something to share? How do you suppose it made him feel after he saw what Jesus did with it?

A VERSE TO LEARN

Give us this day our daily bread. (Matthew 6:11)

LET'S PRAY

Dear God, thank you for letting our food grow in the ground so farmers can gather it and markets can get it and our mothers and fathers can buy it. We know that all food, no matter how we get it, is from YOU in the first place. Help us to share whenever we have a chance and not be stingy and keep everything to ourselves. In Jesus' name. Amen.

CAN YOU FIND THIS STORY IN THE BIBLE?

(Matthew 14:13-21 and Mark 6:32-44 and Luke 9:10-17 and John 6:1-14)

Well, it's quite a problem. These boys want to bring their friend Peter to Sunday School. But Peter lives way off in another direction. And the Sunday School bus doesn't go by his house. What to do? Hmmmm. Have the Superintendent make an announcement and scare up somebody who goes by Peter's way? Hmmmm. Get their fathers to take turns picking Peter up? Hmmm. Well, you may be sure they'll think of SOMETHING. They're Peter's friends and they intend to get him to Sunday School SOMEHOW.

The Man Who Went Through the Roof

The poor man had been sick for years and years. There wasn't a doctor in the world who could heal him. He couldn't even move. Other people had to care for him. Every day was just like every other day. Nothing ever happened.

And then—

one day—

the whole town was all astir. Up one street and down another, people were passing the word along. Jesus was in town!

The friends of the sick man thought, "How wonderful it would be if Jesus would make this poor man well." Then they got busy.

They tied a rope to each corner of his mat-bed so they could carry him. They—hup!—lifted him up and started off to find Jesus. And then they ran into—

TROUBLE.

Jesus wasn't in the market square. He was in a HOUSE —and the crowd was so great they couldn't get in. The men squiggled and they squaggled to try to get through the crowd. No use. They asked people to let them through. Nobody budged. There they stood, with their poor sick friend on his mat-bed, without a chance of ever getting in. There was nothing they could—

WAIT A MINUTE!

There WAS something they could do! It was daring. It was RISKY. But they decided to do it anyhow. They worked their way to the side of the house—to the outside stairs that led up to the roof. And—hup!—up they went, mat-bed and all. The men—oops—made their way carefully across the roof. They made an opening in the roof— and THEN—

They carefully, c-a-r-e-f-u-l-l-y let the sick man down— d-o-w-n—

into the room.

The people in the room looked up. They could hardly believe their eyes! They reached up to grab the mat-bed and backed up to make room for it. And the next thing the poor sick man knew—he was lying right there at Jesus' feet, looking up into Jesus' blessed face! And Jesus looked down at him and said, "Son, thy sins be forgiven thee. Pick up thy bed—and walk."

WALK!

Everybody waited. Jesus had told the sick man to WALK! And that's exactly what the man did. He got up with wonder and rolled up his bed with amazement, and with tear-filled eyes he thanked Jesus. Then as the crowd parted to let him through, he walked right out of that house.

His good friends came leaping down the stairs. And they all met in front of the house and laughed and cried together and probably even hugged each other! How wonderful it was! It was almost too good to be true!

The sick man was now well and oh so happy. Because Jesus, the Son of God, healed him. And because he had friends who CARED enough to BRING him to Jesus!

THINK!

Is there any way you can think of that the sick man could have got to Jesus without his friends? Was there any time along the way that they could have given up? Aren't you glad they didn't? Can you think of any friends who have gone out of their way to take you to Sunday School or Bible School? Have you gone out of your way to take anyone else to where they could learn about Jesus?

A VERSE TO LEARN

By love serve one another. (Galatians 5:13)

180

LET'S PRAY

Dear God, we thank you for every friend we have who cares about us. Help us to be willing to go out of our way to take our friends where they can hear about Jesus. In Jesus' name. Amen.

CAN YOU FIND THIS STORY IN THE BIBLE?

(Matthew 9: 1-8 and Mark 2: 1-12 and Luke 5: 17-26)

Janie is praying. And what she wants is anybody's guess, but she is certainly in a HURRY. "Hurry, hurry, God," she's thinking. Sts, sts, such a business! Imagine trying to make God hurry! Janie will have to learn to WAIT.

The Day Jesus Didn't Hurry

The only one who could help Jairus—was Jesus.

"Hurry, hurry, hurry," thought Jairus, as he left his house. "Hurry, hurry, hurry," he thought as he went through the streets to the lakeside. He HAD to find Jesus. And for a very important reason. His daughter was very, very sick—and if he didn't hurry, she would die.

When Jairus got to the lakeside, the crowd was so great,

his heart nearly stopped beating. Would he be on time? Would Jesus come? "Hurry, hurry, hurry," he thought, as he squeezed his way through the crowd.

Then—at last—there was Jesus!

Jairus ran up to him and fell down at his feet and said, "Oh Jesus—my little girl is so sick she is going to die. Please come and make her well!"

And Jesus said, "Yes, I will go with you."

Oh, joy!

Jairus scrambled to his feet and began to lead the way. "Oh hurry, hurry, hurry," sang in his mind. But the crowds were so great, they COULDN'T hurry. People pressed in on Jesus from every side. Sick people—curious people—nice people—noisy people. They pressed him back and slowed him down. They kept stopping him along the way, some to talk to him—some to just touch his robes. And Jairus thought of his daughter at home, and his mind shouted—"Hurry—HURRY!"

And then—

The worst possible thing happened.

Somebody from Jairus' house broke through the crowd and said, "It's too late! Your daughter is dead. There is no need for Jesus to come." There was no longer any need to hurry.

Jairus looked sadly at Jesus. And Jesus said softly, "Don't be afraid. Just trust me—and I'll help you." And they went on toward Jairus' house.

Jairus didn't hurry now. There was no need to hurry. But he couldn't help wondering. What was Jesus going to DO?

When they got to Jairus' house—Jairus knew the news was true, all right. The house was filled with people—crying. His daughter was dead.

Jesus looked at the people. He looked at poor Jairus. And then he took command. He took the girl's mother and Jairus. He took three of his disciples. And they all went into the girl's room. Nobody else could go in.

There was the girl lying on the bed—and she looked just as if she were sleeping. Jesus went up to her and took her hand—and said—"Little girl, arise."

Jairus held his breath. Nobody in the room made a sound. And then—and then—The girl's eyelashes fluttered.

She began to breathe.

She sat up and looked around.

Then she STOOD UP!

There she was, standing before them—alive, and completely well again!

The only one who could have helped her—was Jesus. And it didn't matter whether he hurried or not. Jesus could do anything. He is the Son of God.

THINK!

Why do you suppose Jesus made Jairus wait? What do you think that taught Jairus? Can you think of times when your mother and dad have told you that you would have to wait for something you wanted very badly? What were the reasons you had to wait? Can you think of times when God has answered your prayers by saying, "Wait. I will give you this at a better time?" Aren't you glad God always answers your prayers in the way he knows is best?

A VERSE TO LEARN

Be not afraid, only believe. (Mark 5:36)

LET'S PRAY

Dear God, help us to be willing to wait and not be in such a hurry every time we want something. Thank you for caring when we're sick. Thank you for our mothers and fathers who care for us when we're sick and when we're well too. And thank you for answering our prayers in the way you know is best. In Jesus' name. Amen.

CAN YOU FIND THIS STORY IN THE BIBLE?

(Matthew 9:18-26 and Mark 5:21-43 and Luke 8:40-56)

Well, saaay! You would never know these were the
same children! They came to choir rehearsal in sneakers—
right from baseball in the back lot. But on Palm Sunday
morning, their hair is slicked down in ALARMING neat-
ness—and their clothes are ironed to a stand-still!* They
look for all the world like a group of angels as they sing
songs of praise and joy. And they really mean it, too! It's
great to praise the Lord on Sunday. But, of course, the
important thing is to praise him all week by behaving
yourself.

An Exciting Day in Jerusalem

The disciples had no way of knowing what an exciting

* This means ironed just *right*.

day this was going to be. It started out just like any other trip.

They left the little village where they had been staying, early in the morning. It was ordinary enough. Just Jesus and his disciples. As they walked along the road, people began to join them. The day was quiet and bright and blue. The disciples could hardly notice the excitement at first. They could just sort of FEEL it beginning.

It began when Jesus asked two of his disciples to go ahead to the next village and get a donkey. "Not just ANY donkey," he told them. "There's a CERTAIN donkey. Untie him and bring him to me."

The disciples went to the village—and it was exactly as Jesus had said. They brought the donkey back to Jesus— and that was when the excitement began to grow a little.

Some of the people took off their bright-colored robes and folded them across the donkey's back for Jesus to sit on. Now Jesus looked like a KING, as they went down the road toward Jerusalem. More and more people began to follow along.

Old people.

Young people.

And CHILDREN.

And the excitement began to grow a little more.

Somebody took off his robe—and spread it on the ground in front of Jesus.

Then somebody else did.

And somebody else.

Then they began to cut branches from palm trees.

And wave them in the air.

And spread them on the road.

Until the road was covered with bright-colored robes and branches and branches and more branches.

Now a sight like that was too exciting for people to keep to themselves. The news spread ahead to Jerusalem. And when Jesus and his disciples got to the gates of Jerusalem —EVERYBODY was out to meet them! And the excitement grew and burst out—
like great swelling MUSIC.

The people were packed on both sides of the streets— the children in front so they could see. And they threw flowers.

And spread out leaves.
And waved palm branches
And sang!

They sang, "Hosanna in the highest. Blessed is he that cometh in the name of the Lord!"

And from the city gates to the great temple with the golden roof—that song was in the air. The children sang it in the streets. They sang it in the temple courts. They filled the air with it. It was one of the most exciting days they'd ever had in Jerusalem. The old people
and young people
and children
all wanted Jesus to know how much they loved him!

And they TOLD him so!

THINK!

Can you think of all the different ways you can praise God in Sunday School? In church? Can you name some ways you can praise him during the week?

A VERSE TO LEARN

Sing unto the LORD with thanksgiving. (Psalm 147:7)

LET'S PRAY

Dear God, we ARE thankful for you. You are so good to us! Help us to behave ourselves—not only on Sunday, but every day in the week. We know that this is one way we can praise you. In Jesus' name. Amen.

CAN YOU FIND THIS STORY IN THE BIBLE?

(Matthew 21:1-17 and Mark 11:1-11 and Luke 19:29-40 and John 12:12-19)

Debbie is having a hard time smiling. And no wonder. Her grandpa is leaving to sail across the ocean to another country. And he isn't going there just to visit. He's going there to LIVE. Debbie doesn't know if she'll EVER see him again. The ship is beautiful. The colored ribbons are gay. And all the people are shouting and waving and laughing. All but Debbie. For this is the saddest day Debbie has ever known in all her LIFE.

The Saddest Day

Oh, that was a glad day, when Jesus rode into Jerusalem on the donkey and people spread their robes and waved palm branches and the children sang and sang until the music seemed to rise to the very skies! It seemed absolutely impossible that anything dreadful could happen after such a glad day.

But it did.

It all began with some people who did not believe that Jesus is the Son of God. It would have been quite dreadful enough if they just didn't believe it, and let it go at that. But they didn't stop there. They sent a band of soldiers after him. And the soldiers caught him in a garden where he was praying to God. And they arrested him and dragged him before the ruler. And the ruler had him tied to a post and whipped. It would have been dreadful enough if they had stopped THERE. But they did not.

When the ruler asked the people what they wanted to do with Jesus—

Some people cried out, "Kill him!"

Then more people cried out, "Kill him!"

Then MORE people cried out, "KILL HIM!"

They cried it out louder and louder and LOUDER.

Until there was such confusion and noise and shouting that it seemed to rise to the very skies, just the way the singing had done on that glad day!

But this was different from the singing. This was different from the glad day.

They made a big wooden cross. They dragged Jesus down into the street. They made him carry the cross through the city. They took him to a hill just outside the city.* And there, on that hill, they nailed him to the cross by his hands and his feet. And they put the cross in a hole in the ground, so it stood up straight and tall. And there they left him to die.

It seemed incredible!* Jesus was dead. JESUS was dead!

It was all over. All the gladness was over.

His friends took him down from the cross. They carried him—oh so tenderly—to a garden tomb.* And there they wrapped him in soft clean cloths. And there they left him.

The soldiers rolled a HUGE stone over the door of the tomb. And Jesus' friends went home.

He was gone. And with him, all the gladness was gone. Jesus' friends felt that there was no more gladness, anywhere in the world, anymore.

* The hill is called the hill of Calvary, and it was just outside the city of Jerusalem.
* This means it's hard to believe.
* The tomb was just like a cave, carved in the rocky hillside.

It was the saddest day in the world. But little did they know—there was a GLAD day coming! Just around the corner! The GLADDEST day in the world!

THINK!

Everything seems to be in a hopeless state. But do you remember way back when Adam and Eve disobeyed God and "spoiled it all?" Go back and read page 11. Why, Jesus left his home in heaven and came to earth to die on the cross because he LOVES you! This is what the Bible means when it says that Jesus Christ came to be your Saviour. Believe it! Let him KNOW you believe it! It's the most wonderful news in the world!

A VERSE TO LEARN

God so loved the world (that means you), *that he gave his . . . Son, that whosoever* (that means you again) *BE-LIEVES in him shall ... have everlasting life.* (John 3:16)

LET'S PRAY

Dear God, we know that from the beginning of the world you planned to have Jesus die for us. And when the time came, it happened, just as you planned it. We thank Jesus for doing this. And we thank YOU for loving us so much that you sent us a Saviour. In Jesus' name. Amen.

CAN YOU FIND THIS STORY IN THE BIBLE?

(Mark 15:1-47 and Luke 23:33-49 and John 19:30)

This is just too much to STAND, it's so GOOD. So HAPPY. So GLAD. Debbie and Craig thought they would never see their grandpa again. But he has come back for a visit. And—oh, joy!—here he is, big as life, hugging them right there on the front door step! He's hugging them so tightly they can hardly BREATHE. And soon he will be opening his suitcases and bringing out goodies for them. The goodies will be great. But the greatest thing of all is having GRANDPA back!

The Gladdest Day

The day started out to be sad. It was still the saddest time in the world for Jesus' friends. Some of them were SO sad that they got up early in the morning and hurried back to the tomb in the garden where they had left him— the tomb with the stone rolled in front of it. They knew it was all over and he was dead. But they had spices and sweet perfumes for him, and they hoped they'd find someone to roll the stone away.

They hurried to the garden, and actually that's all they expected to see. A tomb with a huge stone rolled over the doorway. But when they got there—

The great stone door of the tomb had been rolled away! And Jesus was GONE!

At first they just stood there, STUNNED.

And then they all did different things.

One of them turned on her heels and ran. Her name was Mary Magdalene. And she wasn't just running away. She was running to tell two other special friends.

The rest of them went into the tomb, and—

Surprise of all surprises!

There were two ANGELS inside!

Jesus' friends just stood there, absolutely speechless. They couldn't say a thing.

ANGELS!

And before Jesus' friends could find their voices, the angels said, "He is not dead. He is alive. He is RISEN— just as he told you he would be."

Well, first they just stood there, stunned. And then THEY turned on THEIR heels and ran, just as Mary Magdalene had done.

Then the garden was quiet.

But not for long.

First, the two special friends Mary Magdalene had run to tell, came back. One of them stood and looked in the tomb. The other one went right inside. And sure enough. Everything Mary had told them was true. The cloth Jesus had been wrapped in was there, all neat and in order, and the cloth that had been wrapped around his head was folded neatly. But HE was gone. They went out of the garden, amazed.

Then the garden was quiet again.

But not for long.

For last of all, Mary Magdalene came back. And she stood there by the tomb. And she cried.

"Why are you crying?" asked the angels.

And Mary said, "Because I do not know where Jesus is."

And then—

Suddenly she realized that there was somebody standing just behind her. She turned around. It was a man, but in the early morning half-darkness she did not know him. She thought perhaps he might be the gardener.

"Why are you crying?" he asked. "And who are you looking for?"

"Oh," said Mary, "I'm looking for Jesus. Do YOU know where they have taken him?"

And the stranger said softly—oh so softly and lovingly —"Mary." Just like that.

And the MINUTE he said her name—"Mary"—she knew who he was.

It was JESUS! He was alive! Oh, joy!

"Jesus!" said Mary. It couldn't be true. But it WAS. He was standing right there. He was looking at her. And he SPOKE to her again.

"Go tell my friends that I'm alive," he said, "and that I'm going to heaven—just as I said I would."

And she did!

Oh, it was a GLAD day after all! It was a GLAD day! It was the GLADDEST day in the world!

Do you know what?

It was the first EASTER SUNDAY!

THINK!

Jesus is alive today—the BIBLE tells us so. He is with us, in our hearts. How can we talk to him? How can we listen to him speaking to us? Can you think of some of the many ways he helps you in your own life?

A VERSE TO LEARN

Jesus said, I am with you alway, even unto the end of the world. (Matthew 28:20)

Another verse to learn:

I am alive for evermore. (Revelation 1:18)

LET'S PRAY

Dear God, how we thank you that when we sing the song "Jesus loves me, this I know, for the Bible tells me so," it isn't just a lot of WORDS. The Bible DOES tell us so, and it's all true. How wonderful it is that Jesus is alive and we can talk to each other. We appreciate this, God. And we thank you. In Jesus' name. Amen.

CAN YOU FIND THIS STORY IN THE BIBLE?

(Matthew 28:1-20 and Mark 16:1-20 and Luke 24:1,2 and 13-53)

Chris and Mary Beth are so excited! Daddy has come home with some folders telling all about a far away country they're all going to visit. And there are the most beautiful pictures. Pictures and pictures and MORE pictures. Mountains and lakes and oceans and castles like they have never seen before. They can't make the trip right NOW. But Dad says SOMEDAY for SURE. Oh, joy! What a wonderful thing to look forward to!

The Best News!

Yes, Easter was the gladdest day in the world. Jesus had come out of the tomb alive. Mary had seen him. And she had run to tell all his friends, just as he had asked her to.

And after that they saw him—not every day as they used to—but at the most surprising times!

One time two of them were just walking along the road on their way to a town called Emmaus—and there he was —walking along the road!

One time some of them just got back from fishing all night—and there he was—on the shore!

One time some of them were gathered together in a room in Jerusalem—and there he was—right in the room!

And then, ONE time—

They were with him on the top of a mountain*—when suddenly—

Jesus began to rise up into the air, right before their very eyes! Up—up—UP—until a big cloud covered him up and he was GONE!

Why they just stood there staring at the sky. They were absolutely SPEECHLESS. And while they were staring—

Two angels suddenly stood right alongside them!

"Why are you staring up into heaven?" the two angels said. "Jesus is coming back again. Don't you remember? He's coming back again exactly the same way you just saw him go—through the clouds!"

And then they DID remember.

Of course!

Jesus had told them—a long, LONG time ago that he was going away. And they had been so sad.

"Going away?" they had said. "Going AWAY? O NO!" And then they had all talked at once. "We will go with you," they had said.

And Jesus had looked at their sad faces, and oh, his eyes had been so KIND. "You cannot go with me NOW," he said. "But SOME day, you can."

"Ahhhhh—SOME day," they had thought. And then they had wanted to know—

Where was he going?

* Mount of Olives

198

What was it LIKE?

And he had told them:

"I'm going to get a new home ready for you. It will be more beautiful than this world. More beautiful than anything you have ever SEEN. Or than anything you could even IMAGINE." And he had gone on to tell them about heaven, where no one will ever be sick and no one will ever cry and no one will ever be unhappy. "And some day you can come and live there with me forever," he had said.

Of course!

They remembered, they remembered—

They couldn't be with him NOW. But SOME DAY—

They remembered, they remembered—

And they ran and ran to tell all the people!

THINK!

Everything in the Bible is according to God's plan. He made the world, and it was JUST RIGHT. (Page 1). He planned for Jesus to be born, and he WAS. (Page 143). He planned for Jesus to die for us, and he DID. (Page 190). He planned for Jesus to rise again, and he DID. (Page 193). He planned for Jesus to go back up to heaven and prepare a place for us, and he DID. (Page 197). And he plans for Jesus to come again, and he WILL! Isn't that all good news? And shouldn't you run and run and tell all the people?

A VERSE TO LEARN

Jesus said, *I will come again, and receive you unto myself; that where I am, there ye may be also.* (John 14:3)

LET'S PRAY

Dear God, we thank you that we can be with you some day in heaven. Help us to love you and tell others about you while we're waiting. In Jesus' name. Amen.

CAN YOU FIND THIS STORY IN THE BIBLE?

(Mark 16:19,20 and Luke 24:50-53 and Acts 1:4-9)